Electro-Optical Systems Performance Modeling

The Artech House Optoelectronics Library

Brian Culshaw, Alan Rogers, and Henry Taylor, *Series Editors*

Acousto-optic Signal Processing: Fundamentals and Applications, Pankaj Das

Amorphous and Microcrystalline Semiconductor Devices, Optoelectronic Devices, Jerzy Kanicki, ed.

Electro-Optical Systems Performance Modeling, Gary Waldman and John Wootton

Field Theory of Acousto-Optic Signal Processing Devices, Craig Scott

Highly Coherent Semiconductor Lasers, Motoichi Ohtsu

Introduction to Glass Integrated Optics, S. Iraj Najafi

Optical Control of Microwave Devices, Rainee N. Simons

Optical Fiber Sensors, Volume I: Principles and Components, John Dakin and Brian Culshaw, eds.

Optical Fiber Sensors, Volume II: Systems and Applicatons, Brian Culshaw and John Dakin, eds.

Optical Network Theory, Yitzhak Weissman

Principles of Modern Optical Systems, Volume I, I. Andonovic and D. Uttamchandani, eds.

Principles of Modern Optical Systems, Volume II, I. Andonovic and D. Uttamchandani, eds.

Reliability and Degradation of LEDs and Semiconductor Lasers, Mitsuo Fukuda

Electro-Optical Systems Performance Modeling

Gary Waldman
John Wootton

Artech House
Boston • London

Library of Congress Cataloging-in-Publication Data

Waldman, Gary.
    Electro-optical systems performance modeling / Gary Waldman, John Wootton.
       p.   cm.
    Includes bibliographical references and index.
    ISBN 0-89006-541-1
    1. Electrooptical devices—Mathematical models.
2. System analysis. I. Wootton, John. II. Title.

TA1750.W32   1992   92-18850
621.36'7—dc20   CIP

© 1993 ARTECH HOUSE, INC.
685 Canton Street
Norwood, MA 02062

International Standard Book Number: 0-89006-541-1
Library of Congress Catalog Card Number: 92-18850

10 9 8 7 6 5 4 3 2 1

To Mary Lou, Rachel, Jennifer, and David
Pamela, Matthew, and Scott

Contents

Preface

This book is a reflection of the lifetime work of the authors in the field of *electro-optical* (EO) system design and analysis, including the mathematical modeling of these systems.

As practicing engineers we have found it useful to have at our fingertips many rules of thumb, many models, and many reference books. When we were eventually called upon a few years ago to teach our company's next generation of designer-analysts, we could find no central source for all this data. As part of this course we attempted to bring together all these diverse sources in lecture notes and to skip over some of the more detailed work in order to provide the student sufficient depth to prevent him or her falling into some dangerous pitfalls, yet not so much as to clutter the mind with superfluous knowledge that might detract from an essential grasp of the subject.

This book started out with the same premise and in fact is based on those earlier lecture notes. However, we have expanded certain sections to reach a slightly more general audience. This book could serve for not only practicing EO systems designers, analysts, modelers, and model users, but also as part of a graduate or undergraduate course of study in this area.

ACKNOWLEDGMENTS

The authors wish to acknowledge both the tangible and intangible contributions of various people to this publication.

It is appropriate that the first acknowledgment go to our longtime friend and colleague, Harry Nelgner. Harry was not only a gracious coworker on some of our original work, but was also an inspiration to all who aspired to be technically sound practitioners in the world of electro-optics.

We wish to thank Dr. Iwasa Sato of LORAL Honeywell for his careful reading of the draft manuscript, his constructive criticism, and helpful suggestions. Any remaining errors or deficiencies in the work, however, must be claimed by the authors.

Finally we want to thank the staff at Artech House, and in particular, Pamela Ahl whose kindly guidance and encouragement made possible the production of this book.

Chapter 1
Introduction and Overview

In the beginning God created the Heaven and the Earth.
And the Earth was without form and void; and darkness was upon the face of
the deep. And the Spirit of God moved upon the face of the waters.
And God said, "Let there be light," and there was light.
And God saw the light, that it was good; and God divided the light from the
darkness.
And God called the light Day, and the darkness he called Night. And the
evening and the morning were the first day.

1.1 INTRODUCTION

This book was written from the over a half-century of collective experience of the authors in support of military electro-optical systems. During the last decade, we have cooperated on specifying practical visible and infrared systems. Most recently, we have been active in passing on this knowledge through a series of short courses. As an addition to the courses, we looked for a single reference book that would support the context of the seminars. To our dismay, among the plethora of good books on the single disciplines, we found none that encompassed all the disciplines that a system engineer encounters.

This book was written to fill the void. It was written specifically for system engineers and system designers with responsibilities ranging from selecting an appropriate electro-optical solution to meet some higher-level requirements to evaluating the performance of some available hardware again to meet some overall system requirement goals.

It is not intended to be an optical designer's manual. The reader will be no better equipped to undertake real optical design after reading this book than at the beginning. On the other hand, he or she will be better equipped to understand some of the considerations that a designer accommodates in coming up with a design and, more important, the significance of those parameters. The reader should be better equipped to give detailed specifications to such an optical designer.

The book covers a fairly wide range of subjects, at a modest depth for each particular discipline. The underlying theme is an in-depth study of the overall problem of electro-optical systems. No one book could cover the total span of all a system designer could be called upon to address. We have used our judgment to trim the book to the more usual set of problems that the systems engineer will encounter. The depth of knowledge presented has therefore been compromised. Mainly, it is neither so shallow that the reader stumbles on his or her first problem, nor is it so deep that inordinate effort is consumed in building an overly large and, for the most part, redundant foundation of knowledge. The latter compromise, however, has not been too severe. The book is written for engineers, mathematicians, and physicists alike. With a good basis in any one of these subjects and a thorough reading of this text, the material presented can be mastered. There is no prerequisite specialization in the theory of optics. There is, however, no substitute for a solid knowledge foundation in all disciplines and plenty of practice in the arena of system engineering.

Throughout this brief introduction we have repeatedly used the term *electro-optical systems*. These are systems that convert photons to electrons, regardless of wavelength. Thus *electro-optical systems* will encompass not only the visible band, but also the *infrared* (IR) and the *ultraviolet* (UV) bands. The wavelengths associated with these will be examined in Figure 2.1.

The book serves as a modestly in-depth introduction to the subject of electro-optical modeling and, we hope, stimulates the reader to look further into the subject and to try a few practical designs. Having acquired the knowledge, we encourage the reader to try a few examples from existing system designs. We suggest you come up with your own solution then compare it with what was produced. The analysis of the difference in the designs will be illuminating. Maybe a system design requirement was missed by the originator or by yourself—sometimes these requirements are not always obvious or recorded (e.g., size constraints, aperture, weight, *et cetera*).

1.2 WHY THE EMPHASIS ON ELECTRO-OPTICAL SYSTEM ENGINEERING?

We live in an everchanging and evolving world. Only a few decades ago any practical discussion of military imaging systems focused entirely on a purely optical system, limited in dynamic range to the ability of the eye from bright sunlight to dark adaptation. These early target acquisition devices became fire control devices only when human beings entered the loop. Then, with the addition of daylight TV, these electro-optical systems provided not only the displayed video for target acquisition, but also the electronic signal for the early TV tracking of fire control systems. The advent of an electronic adjunct to the hard optical solution brought new dimensions to this particular sensor wavelength.

Radar and infrared sensors started development at various locations throughout the world just prior to World War II. Primarily due to the initial success of primitive radar, infrared was relegated almost to laboratory interest until the 1960s. Since then, it has had a stimulating growth. However, in some respects it still suffers from the initial decision of many governments to pursue radar development rather than infrared development many years ago. Knowledge and education are the only way of easing the stigma still associated with imaging systems and their performance. Critical to that issue is the need to educate people into asking the right system questions. This revolves around specifying a requirement and not a solution, however subtly it is implied. We will not dwell on this issue here, but it is such an important concept to the system engineer that the next subsection of this first chapter is dedicated to the concept of specifying a true requirement.

The development of infrared has allowed the military to observe the battlefield at night. In a parallel time frame, image intensifiers came along, which also permitted battlefield observation in the visible band at night. From a system engineering perspective, these breakthroughs were significant. Instead of having a sensor capable of target acquisition and fire control with an availability of 50%, we now had electro-optical systems with complete day-night coverage. Although being able to operate in the dark has grown in prominence, we feel that it has always been more significant than has been accredited. In most theoretical evaluation procedures, we assume that there are 12 hours of daylight and 12 hours of dark. This is really true only on the equator. As one progresses, north or south, this becomes closer to six months of light and six months of dark. The question of assigned sensor availability of 50% might be true on the equator; one would be hard pressed to make the same assignment in the northern part of Norway!

Optics and sensors have continued to evolve. However, it is still true that the principal recipient of the output of these systems is a human being. It is undoubtedly true that the 1980s has seen the staggering growth in capability of *automatic target cuers* (ATCs) and *recognizers* (ATRs). We anticipate that the 1990s will bring similar growth in automatic multisensor systems. When we talk of today's fielded systems, the prime decision maker—the target acquisition device—for imaging sensors is still the human being. When evaluating today's electro-optical systems, therefore, it is necessary to talk in terms of the probabilities of detection, recognition, classification, and identification achieved by a human using these systems. The essential objective of this book is to show the reader how to perform such analyses, together with a choice of appropriate models. Although the basic concepts are extendable to the evaluation of electro-optical systems using automatic target cuers and recognizers and although we have considerable experience in this field, these subjects will not be covered in this present book.

1.3   UNDERSTANDING THE TRUE REQUIREMENTS

A consistent theme throughout this book is the system's approach to electro-optical modeling. Figure 1.1 will provide a framework of elements from which the reader may visualize many of the concepts we will be dealing with. The model provided in Figure 1.1 shows the interdependence of all these elements, target and background, atmosphere, electro-optical system, display, and the human performance limitations on the overall probability of detection, identification, or classification of a target in a given background. This generic structure is appropriate whether we are differentiating between the observability of various targets against various backgrounds, considering the capability of various visible or infrared sensors to detect any one of those objects, considering the impact of atmospherics on the

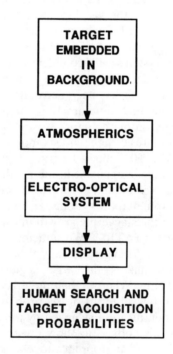

Figure 1.1 Elements of electro-optical systems modeling.

overall outcome, or determining the impact an expected volume coverage would have in detection time.

For most applications, system engineers are really interested only in the impact of a system parameter change on the overall performance. The overall performance evaluation parameters are described in fairly straightforward terms, such as time or range to achieve a certain probability of detection, recognition, or classification. However, a multitude of parameters, as will be discussed in the next section, affect the overall performance. The number of such variables, although large, is nevertheless finite, which should have led the industry to a consistent methodology to perform evaluations. Such is not the case, and any attempt to unify the procedure has led to much controversy and much debate, with little constructive outcome. The lack of a consistent methodology to provide an overall believable figure-of-merit for a given system parameter change has led the industry to focus on the parameter change itself. The drive to develop a better *forward looking infrared* (FLIR) system is often measured in terms of improved *minimum resolvable temperature difference* (MRTD), because this is a tangible, measurable figure that the FLIR manufacturer is most familiar with. However, its real worth should be measured in terms of improved detection range or time to detect a given target under a given scenario. Thus, from a system perspective, the worth of such increases in range or detection time can be evaluated. Similarly, when we discuss the camouflaging of targets by, say, reducing their infrared signature from 10° to 5° to 2.5° delta T, we can establish the value of doing that, not in terms of the signature itself, but in terms of the real objective, which is to reduce detection range or time. As, we will see later in this book, the relationship is far from linear, any linear change in a parameter is unlikely to have a linear change in the outcome. Equally so to change a parameter such as the delta T, the relationship of the equivalent temperature difference of the target signature to the background, from 10° to 5° and from 5° to 2.5°, is itself far from linear. As one approaches the lower limits the law of diminishing returns becomes all too obvious; and the more mature is a technology area, the more prevalent is this law.

We as system engineers should always strive to obtain meaningful answers to our questions in terms of the true requirements and not in terms of solutions. We must ask ourselves whether there are any underlying assumptions in the specifications of the requirements themselves. Constraining requirements often reduce large trade-off studies in system engineering, but it also often guides the system engineer to a preordained solution. We need to guard against being driven by our background prejudices. Over many years we have found that radar system engineers find only a radar solution to a target acquisition problem and correspondingly electro-optical system engineers invariably find only electro-optical solutions. We are all preprogrammed by our background and knowledge. Rules of thumb are correspondingly useful and dangerous. Therefore, although, for instance, radar often affords longer coverage and faster scan coverage in all weather conditions, this is not universally true; and when the requirements include such crucial specifications as stationary target detection and classification, radar often falls short of its electro-optical counterparts. It is not our intent here to prejudge the ability of radar or infrared or visible sensors, rather it is to emphasize that the real system requirement should not include any reference to the solution.

At the risk of being redundant we urge every system designer to start a design by writing down the actual requirements, explicitly stating any implied variables. Start at the generic level but be as specific as possible. By way of example, a requirement might be expressed as a need to develop a target acquisition system to detect military threats on the battlefield from a ground vehicle platform. The requirement at this stage is still fairly generic and provides no real guidelines as to the appropriateness of a solution. It is essentially an empty requirement. To be able to proceed further we need to be a little more specific. Can the target acquisition device be a single sensor or are multiple sensors allowable? Is there a question of whether the sensor should be passive or active? Is there a question of search range or volume? Are the atmospheric conditions definable? Do any *battlefield induced contaminants* (BIC) need to be accounted for? Is there a single target or multiple targets; is it a single type or are there multiple target types (tank, truck, armored personnel carriers, helicopters, and so on)? What is the signature of those target types: size, shape, camouflage? What is the background type. Does the platform itself yield any constraints, like weight or size limitations? Does the platform exhibit any vibration? Considerations concerning such issues as cost, reliability, survivability, environmental factors, and so forth should also be explicitly stated. Finally, any hard constraints that exclude solutions or soft constraints that will weigh heavily in any trade-off studies should be recorded. For instance, a specific payload limit in weight might be a driving issue on such platforms as a *remotely piloted vehicle* (RPV) whereas, it would be of secondary importance on, say, a 50-ton tank.

There is often a fine line between stating the requirement explicitly and providing the solution. Great care has to be exercised at the requirements stage not to do this. Early in the preceding specification, the system designer, in an attempt to be more specific, could have stated the need for an infrared imaging target acquisition system to detect military threats. Such a requirement could not be interpreted as being more explicit than the original generic statement (unless, of course, having a FLIR was a real requirement); it merely is an assumption of the answer and a restriction on the solution. At this stage, we will not attempt to belabor the point, however, we urge all system engineers to write down the real requirements without regard to the final solution. After many trade-offs, conscious or otherwise, and an appropriate solution has been derived, it is often a humbling moment to run the solution against these written requirements. It is occasionally a proud moment when the final solution meets the requirements and does not comply with the original "seat-of-the-pants" first cut!

To be able to be more specific about the requirements, it is necessary to understand the variables that have an impact on the final solution. As this book is about understanding electro-optical systems, the next section will form an introduction to some of these variables. This section forms only a framework on which the rest of the book provides a continuing detailed explanation.

1.4 UNDERSTANDING THE IMPLIED VARIABLES

This book will cover only the visible and infrared parts of the electro-optical spectrum. The visible part extends from 400 nm to 750 nm, and the infrared systems covers both the 3–5 μm and the 8–12 μm bands. This book covers only passive, imaging systems.

As discussed in the previous section, it behooves the system designer to be as specific as possible when approaching a system trade-off. To do this a designer must concentrate on those variables that have a first-order impact on the particular design. In some cases it is necessary to extend trade-offs to second-order effects, but only when all first-order effects have been accommodated. A suggested list of typical variables is shown in Table 1.1. The significance of these variables will depend on the particular application; however, in general these are all of first-order significance, and any evaluation tool or model should encompass these variables. It is important to focus in on first making sure we have an adequate definition

Table 1.1
Pertinent System Variables

Line of sight	Search time
Object movement	System optics
Object size	Collector efficiency (transmission)
Object temperature	Wavelength range
Object paint	Magnification
Contrast	Aperture
Emissivity	F-number
Reflectivity	MTF
Background	Sensor
Emissivity	Sensitivity
Reflectivity	Noise
Homogeneity, clutter	MTF
Illumination, sun	Resolution
Time of day	Dynamic Range
Temperature	Display
Range	Human performance
Atmosphere	Eyesight
Search sector	Fatigue

of the problem and any constraints that are pertinent. It is often necessary to extend the evaluation beyond just optical tools. For effectiveness it may be necessary to extend the analyses to wargame models to find the operational benefit of, say, an extended detection range. It is further necessary to evaluate the significance of physical constraints such as size or weight or, of increasing importance, cost. All too often the preferred system solution comes up with a larger aperture than can be physically accommodated. A larger aperture solution also results when the search volume required in a given time is omitted from the design specifications. The dimension of variables within a problem may be large with no single equation to link all the variables. System engineering by its nature is a compromise; what might be optimum for one set of circumstances is invariably not under another set of conditions. The variables in Table 1.1 can be used as the start of a checklist when approaching a design specification.

Table 1.1 gives an indication of the dimensionality of the problem, yet it gives no indication of the pertinence of any of the variables. In discussions one becomes sensitized to the fact that the performance of a system (in which a human is the ultimate decision maker) is strongly linked to the human's performance. As a result, in mid-1983 we [1] started to refine our understanding of human perception and those dominant factors or elements within a scene that define the degree of difficulty for the task of detecting a target. For each element a syntactical descriptor was offered. However, the real strength of this work was the normalized numerical descriptor of each element that evolved. A scene may then be categorized as a set of vector components representing excursions along each element in an abstract space. It is our intent to be able to parametrically define any scene according to the degree of difficulty of finding a given object in it. This degree is based on a series of elementary considerations. It is evident that the target and scene elements are dependent variables, however, we can normalize the majority of the variables against the sensor's ability to discriminate on the basis of contrast and spatial extent. We perceive that the major elements determining the degree of difficulty of locating a target of interest are as given in Table 1.2.

The first two factors are clearly in a class by themselves. A target with no contrast against the background is impossible to locate. Size is of a significance similar to contrast. The next three elements modify the degree of difficulty in finding a target; however, their unit vector length is constrained by the spatial extent and contrast components. Shape is particularly difficult to quantify but can be considered a modification of the clutter definition. The number of targets alters the interpretation of results. Color can be considered as extending the contrast definition, using the spectral dependence of contrast. All these factors will be discussed throughout the book. Any *electro-optical* (EO) system model or model variations should allow the user to evaluate the overall system performance in the face of the variables listed in Tables 1.1 and 1.2.

Table 1.2
Scene Elements Determining the Degree of Difficulty

Scene Factors	Order of Importance			
	First	*Second*	*Third*	*Fourth*
1	Target size			
2	Contrast			
3		Clutter		
4		Movement		
5		Shape		
6			Number	
7				Color

In addition to the somewhat academic evaluation of performance the electro-optical system designer has to be concerned with other evaluation elements, such as are listed in Table 1.3. It is advisable to use Tables 1.1 through 1.3 as an initial checklist for specifying electro-optical sensors. Such a checklist should also be accompanied by an appropriate weighting for evaluation purposes. This weighting in general is not linear and will be exaggerated as parameters of a given system approach a constraint.

It should be evident to the reader that the expectations of capability of an electro-optical system designer is extremely broad. A system designer in either the visible or IR system field must master seven basic disciplines:

Table 1.3
Other Considerations for Evaluations

Size
Weight
Cost
Power
Availability
Design maturity
Environmental capabilities:
   Thermal range
   Shock
   Vibration
Quality
Reliability
Built-in-test capability
Maintainability
Logistic support

1. Radiation theory target size and target-to-background and intrinsic contrast.
2. Atmospheric spectral transmissions.
3. Optical design.
4. Detector (and, for IR systems, detector cooler) operations.
5. Electronic signal processing.
6. Video display.
7. Human search processes (and, for FLIR systems, visual perception).

When analyzing any visible or IR system there is a natural progression (see Figure 1.1), starting with ascertaining the target signature as seen against the background. The target has a spatial extent (size) as well as contrast. The intrinsic contrast is generally degraded by the path of radiation through the atmosphere. The radiation is received by the imaging system. It is interesting to note that if nature in the form of atmosphere has already reduced the contrast to an indeterminate level it does not matter what sensor is used to detect the object. All systems, for comparative evaluation purposes, should start out with the same received radiant energy at the input to the optics. The imaging system consists of a set of optics to focus the radiant energy onto a detector that is spectrally responsive to the energy. The detector converts the energy of the photons to an electrical voltage or current, which in turn is amplified, processed, and clocked out at some standard video frame rate to drive and illuminate the display monitor. The human observes the display and makes judgments about the presence of potential targets according to displayed contrast and size of objects within the scene.

We will discuss more on models in Chapter 8 of this book. However, one should not run away with the idea that models are the total answer to the design problems. Lloyd [2] points out that at least 40 potential factors, subdivided into five main categories, must be considered in a design. The five categories he lists are

1. Displayed target characteristics (14 considerations).
2. Displayed scene characteristics (4 considerations).
3. System characteristics (6 considerations).
4. Observer states (11 considerations).
5. Tactical and miscellaneous factors (5 considerations).

Many of these factors are covered by some models, but not all.

1.5 MODELING PHILOSOPHY

The key to the electro-optical system engineering process and a central theme of this book is the development of a series of appropriate models. As this thematic sentence embodies several crucial elements of this book, it is of value to enlarge on some of these aspects here.

First, it should be noted that models are a prerequisite of any systematic study. (Note that the word is in the plural.) Models are the tools of the system designer. To have but one tool is to be like a carpenter having only a saw; one rapidly runs out of tasks one can reasonably accomplish. If you add to that basic tool correspondingly unsophisticated tools such as a hammer and chisel much more can be accomplished, including products of real value. A carpenter who adds yet more sophisticated tools such as routers and lathes can become a virtuoso in wood. We do not want to draw from the analogy too closely but it emphasizes yet another aspect of modeling, knowing when it is appropriate to use a model. As the carpenter has to choose the right tool for the right task and know how to use that tool, so the system designer has the same responsibility. When this is realized much of the controversy over which electro-optical model or which procedure is better no longer is an issue. There are many electro-optical models, just as there are many carpenter's tools; the optimum choice depends on the task at hand and what the tool was initially designed to achieve.

This latter point gives further emphasis to the issue of appropriateness. In everyday life we are surrounded by models that are in some way a simplified analogy of reality. An appropriate model addresses those critical issues for which it is designed. The underlying assumption is that certain details have little impact on the situation being modeled.

We have attempted to underscore the significance of developing, choosing, and using models appropriate for a specific application. When developing models it pays to have specific objectives in mind; otherwise the crucial trade-off of the significance of including a given parameter to the final model cannot be made wisely. Here we face a fundamental difficulty in writing a book such as this. It is necessary for us to make some assumptions as to the needs of the reader; to do this we have leaned heavily on our experience. We hope that throughout the text we clearly indicate the purpose and use of any "ready-made" models described.

While covering the general theme of modeling we would like to elucidate on a few more issues related to modeling. A system model must have integrity and be manageable. The desire for integrity is fairly obvious; we want to believe the results. The desire for manageability should stem from a desire to understand the results. There is always a tendency in modeling to model the part of the problem that is extremely well understood to a very high degree yet give only surface thought to those factors that may not be so well understood, even though these latter factors may play a much more significant role in the outcome than the former. In the area of electro-optical systems modeling perhaps the most complex subcomponent, and equally least understood, is the human performance model. In many models this process is represented by a probability of detection as a simple function of the single variable, observed spatial size of target. Within the same models one will see multiple, faceted targets and backgrounds, extensive atmospheric models, and the electro-optical sensor characteristics modeled to very high spectral and spatial resolutions. The result is an unbalanced model that addresses higher-order effects while missing the lower-order ones. Results obtained from such models show a difference when changing these higher-order effects but they really have no significance in terms of the accuracy of the model. We should always strive for a balanced model.

For a model to be manageable it should model all first-order effects and all corresponding lower-order effects and their interactions down to the resolution of the desired results. Models that play only first-order effects are useful in rapid trade-off studies, reducing solutions to only a few final solutions. When the accuracy or resolution of the model cannot differentiate the solutions, either the difference is insignificant or models with higher (second, third, *et cetera*) order effects (i.e., higher-resolution models) need to be applied. Again, in a system designer's tool box it is often appropriate to have models that address the same issue but are of different resolution. This enables rapid elimination of many issues while maintaining clear focus on why such systems have been eliminated.

1.6 SPATIAL *versus* FREQUENCY DOMAIN ANALYSIS

A great deal of concern and discussion focuses on the methodology of modeling electro-optical systems. There seem to be two camps, as it were, each of which sings the praises of one particular approach: the spatial and frequency domain approaches. The latter seems, without question, to be the more common approach; and for a singularly good reason, the spatial frequency approach is excellent for linear systems analysis. It has the advantage that, when the MTF of a given part of a system is known, it can be combined with a simple multiplication with the remaining components of the system to give the overall *modulation transfer function* (MTF). It should be pointed out, however, that although it is excellent for the modeling of the electro-optical device itself, when we extend our needs to a full-system representation, including the human element, its advantages are not so evident. Its limitations are basically twofold. First of all, the combination of spatial frequency domain components by the simple multiplication of their MTFs to give an overall MTF is strictly true only for linear system design. With infrared systems, one invariably talks about ac-coupled devices, and therefore one should be very careful with this methodology; and whereas it might appear to be linear for small excursions away from a given data point, extensions or projections of models any distance away from these data points should be questioned. However, of greater significance is the second issue, the overall performance of electro-optical systems. This is defined not in terms of the MTF of the overall system but in terms of the detection or recognition capabilities of that system as afforded by human beings. Here it should be noted that the overwhelming psychophysical experimentation on human acquisition is in the spatial domain. Very little work on acquisition probabilities, with the exception of one famous set of experimental data [3], has been performed in the frequency domain. This subject will be discussed at length later; however, at this stage we should note that we can in fact mix the methodologies of both the spatial domain approach and the frequency domain approach. This can simply be done by representing the target as a bar pattern, then treating the contrast reduction and so on through the electro-optical system by using the frequency domain approach, registering the effect in the spatial domain, and finally using the spatial domain with all the accompanying psychophysical data experimentation to evaluate the human perception.

Rather than preempt the later chapter on end-to-end models, Chapter 8, we will not discuss this aspect any further than to say that both spatial and frequency domain methodologies will be discussed as well as methodologies for mixing both to derive maximum advantages of both.

1.7 PARAMETRIC ANALYSIS MODELING *versus* SYNTHETIC VIDEO REPRESENTATION

The realization that the probability of detection or recognition depends on so many variables has caused the creation of yet another school of thought in the arena of electro-optical system designers. This new school concentrates its efforts in generating synthetically the full image as would be seen by the operator using a TV camera or a FLIR. This image is a pixel-by-pixel representation of the video that would come from a sensor of a real or synthetically generated scene with a real or synthetic target embedded in that scene. The intrinsic contrasts of the displayed objects are appropriately degraded by the atmosphere and the MTF of the sensors and platform. Evaluation of the sensor is made either by subjecting a number of observers to the displayed video or recording the degradation in terms of number of lines on target and interpreting the result into a probability of detection.

The existence of synthetic video simulation as a tool for system evaluation would not warrant further comment were it not for the vehemence with which a core of those involved in such simulation argue that it is the only (valid) methodology of design and evaluation of electro-optical systems. Whereas there is little question of the depth of integrity with which many of these synthetic models are generated, their usefulness as a stand-alone system design and evaluation tool has to be questioned. It is necessary to realize that, when dealing with system designs and the various trade-offs an electro-optical designer faces, it is dangerous to particularize on a given scene. It is much better to be able to characterize a scene with some appropriate metric, and thereafter the analysis will be appropriate for the whole ensemble of scenes that correspond to that metric. It is of more value to find scene metrics that allow for a range of scenes to be described parametrically. The existence of such scene metrics, as described later in this book, allows rapid generalized meaningful trade-offs to be undertaken. Synthetic video simulation should be regarded as one of the tools for the electro-optical system designer but it should be kept more as a tool for evaluating or anticipating the image from the selected system rather than a tool for providing the initial selection of the appropriate TV or infrared system.

1.8 OVERVIEW OF THE BOOK

This first chapter forms an introduction and an overview of the subject of electro-optical system design. It attempts to introduce the reader to the dimensionality and the complexity of the considerations undertaken by the designer. It also serves as a caution to the designer to ensure the unbiased statement of the true requirement. Chapter 2 provides a somewhat qualitative feel for differing types of electro-optical and infrared sensors. It discusses the basic wavelength issues and provides definitions of baseline hardware solutions. Chapter 3 deals with the basic physics required for understanding the remainder of the book. It provides a key chapter on sources and transfer of radiation, both photometric and radiometric. Armed with the background and understanding of the first three chapters, the remaining chapters follow the outline of a generic model given earlier in this chapter. Sequentially, Chapters 4 through 7 deal with target and background models, atmospheric effects, modeling sensors, and human observers. To round off the book, Chapter 8 deals with end-to-end models, including quick reaction models, as well as detail models. Readers familiar with the background of electro-optical and FLIR sensors and who have a thorough understanding of the transfer of radiation will find it expedient to skip to Chapter 4.

REFERENCES

1.   G. Waldman, J. Wootton, G. Hobson, K. Luetkemeyer, "A Normalized Clutter Measure for Images," *Comp. Vis., Graphics, and Image Proc.*, Vol. 42, 1988, p. 137.
2.   J.M. Lloyd, *Thermal Imaging Systems*, Plenum Press, New York, 1975, pp. 388–390.
3.   J. Johnson, "Analysis of Image Forming Systems," *Proc. Symp. on the Image Intensifier*, Fort Belvoir, VA, D 220160, 1958, p. 249.

Chapter 2
Qualitative Discussion of Sensors

This chapter is dedicated to a qualitative investigation of passive electro-optical sensors. The main theme of this chapter is preceded by an introduction to the visible and IR wavelengths. Understanding the issues surrounding wavelengths is a key to anticipating some of the capabilities and limitations of this technology. This chapter continues with a discussion of both TV sensors (including daylight, low-light TV, and color) and IR sensors (with emphasis on FLIRs). It discusses the state of the art in both parts of the spectrum together with future trends. The subject is pertinent in that practicing system engineers should thoroughly under-stand the devices and the limitations of the devices being modeled. As this chapter revolves around practical hardware without unduly emphasizing the underlying theory it is the one chapter that will date the book. With that forewarning we will try to be as contemporary as is possible.

2.1 WAVELENGTH ISSUES

A useful starting point when discussing EO systems is to look at where certain bands occur in the electromagnetic spectrum and why these bands were chosen. Confusing to many is the fact that charts are printed with either the frequency increasing left to right or with the wavelength increasing left to right. Radio and radar engineers express themselves primarily in frequency, whereas IR and visible systems engineers express themselves in wavelengths. Wavelengths and frequency are linked by the simplest of equations:

$$\lambda f = c \tag{2.1}$$

where

λ = wavelength (in same length units as c)
f = frequency (Hz)
c = velocity of light = 3×10^8 m/s.

Table 2.1 lists some of the more commonly known frequency bands with their associated wavelengths.

In terms of wavelength, the ultraviolet band covers the 1 nm (nanometer) to 400 nm band. The visible band extends from 400 nm to 750 nm. The near infrared covers the 750 nm to 3 μm band, the mid-infrared extends from the 3 μm band to the 30 μm band, and the far infrared band covers the 30 μm band to about 1000 μm or 1 mm wavelength band.

The spectrum is a continuous band. We will be investigating visible systems from 400 nm to 750 nm and IR systems primarily in two bands, the 3–5 μm band and the 8–12 μm band. For their relationship on the electromagnetic scale, see Figure 2.1.

The underlying physics is reserved for Chapter 3, however, there is a commonly held opinion that the basis of visible systems and IR systems has no common link, indeed that the former is linked to the physics of photons whereas the latter is linked to the physics of heat. Nothing can be further from the truth. Visible and IR systems both deal with the physics of photons. Photons are generated with a total radiant flux proportional to absolute temperature to the fourth power (Stefan-Boltzmann law) and with a peak energy wavelength inversely proportional to temperature (Wien's displacement law). The only real differences between a visual image and an IR image is that (1) the natural visual spectrum image is produced primarily by reflection and reflectivity differences whereas thermal images are produced primarily by self-emission and emissivity differences, and (2) the IR wavelength is considerably longer than the visual wavelength.

In the visible band we have a very powerful hot illuminator, the sun. The sun's temperature is around 5600 °C (or 5875 K). The sun's energy peaks at about 550 nm. Remarkably 38% of the sun's radiant energy is in the band of 0.4 μm (400 nm) to 0.75 μm (750 nm) (18% being below 400 nm and 46% being above 750 nm). Interesting to note also is that 94% of the radiant energy from the sun

Table 2.1
Electromagnetic Spectrum

Band Name	Frequency	Wavelength
AM broadcast	750 kHz	400 m
Shortwave radio	50 MHz	6 m
UHF TV	500 MHz	60 cm
	3 GHz	10 cm
X band radar	10 GHz	3 cm
MMW	100 GHz	3 mm
IR	21.4–37.5 THz	14–8 μm
	60–100 THz	5–3 μm
Light	400–750 THz	.7–.4 μm

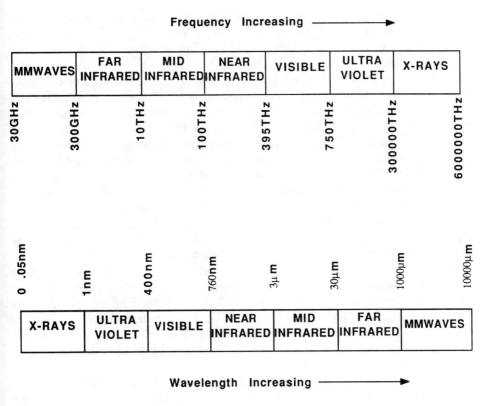

Figure 2.1 The electromagnetic spectrum.

is below 2 μm and only 2% of the total sun's energy exists above 3 μm. It is fortunate that terrestrial materials have good reflective properties in the 400 nm to 750 nm band. The basic detector in the visible band is the human eye. The eye's spectral response almost coincides with the shape of the sun's spectral response and peaks at about the same peak of 550 nm. The eye is quite remarkable; nature has obviously done its homework with respect to the physics of the situation. The eye is an ideal quantum-noise–limited device; the retinal radiation detectors (both rods and cones) have low noise at the quantum energy levels in this band. Furthermore, the response of these retinal detectors to the photons emitted at body temperatures of 98.6 °F is negligible. During the day we have an illuminator (the sun) that gives peak energy in the visible spectrum; most terrestrial objects efficiently reflect this energy, and the eye acts as an uncooled spectrally matched detector.

During the night, however, the sun is no longer a direct illuminator. The moon is a poor reflector of the sun, reflecting less than 7% of the energy falling on it. Therefore little illumination is available. For effective sensors at night we have a few choices. We can go for image intensification in the visible band or we can look to the longer IR wavelength detectors to provide images of the scene differences. Where historically many engineers have become confused is that systems looking in the IR band are usually described in terms of temperature differences rather than radiometric differences. If you took a thermometer you could not measure that actual temperature difference between one part of the scene and another. The original intention was that, if all the scene temperatures, reflectivities, and emissivities contributions were taken together at a point in the scene, they could be represented by an effective temperature at that point. This effective temperature is the temperature of some blackbody placed at that point in the scene whose radiance is equivalent to the scene-measured radiance. Similarly, the irradiance measured through an intervening atmosphere may be thought of as being produced by an apparent temperature somewhat less than the effective temperature. It is pertinent to note that, apart from leaving quite a lot of confusion, such a simplifying analogy is possible only because most thermal images have broad spectral bands and accept all polarizations. The latter condition will change when IR cameras are made polarization sensitive. Then the camera will be sensitive to polarization effects of reflected IR energy. Such a simple equivalent blackbody temperature analogy (which deals with the emissive nature of bodies) no longer will hold true.

Visual systems are therefore concerned with the reflected sun's radiation, and IR systems are concerned more with self-emissions of objects. Nevertheless, there is remarkable similarity between both systems. Both systems are concerned with reflected and self-emitted radiation; it is just that as the wavelength changes so does the dominance of the various items. All systems are concerned with the detection of photons.

2.1.1 Why the Choice of Various Spectral Bands?

In the visible part of the spectrum we see objects because of their reflectance of the sun's emitted radiance. The sun, as can be seen by Figure 2.2, can be considered an almost perfect blackbody at 5900 K. As a result of its path through the atmosphere, certain portions of its energies are absorbed. The eye, as mentioned earlier, is matched spectrally to this energy; see Figure 2.3.

In the absence of this wonderful illuminator we have to use the spectral emissions of the object itself. The first military objects IR systems were used to detect were the hot exhaust gases of aircraft engines. Those gases, which had temperatures between 600 and 1000 K, had their peak wavelengths between 2.898

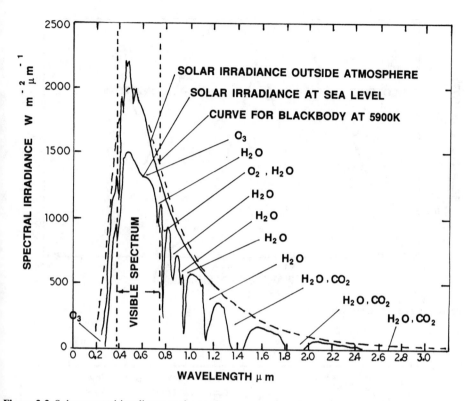

Figure 2.2 Solar spectral irradiance at the earth.

μm and 4.833 μm, see Figure 2.4. This was rather fortunate, in that the atmosphere has a transmission window from 3 to 5 μm.

As thermal imagers were challenged to detect ground-based targets, which characteristically had temperatures around the 300 K, reference to Figure 2.4 or a radiation slide rule will show that the total radiation is small (4.6 × 10⁻² W/cm² compared with 5.5 W/cm² at 1000 K) and that less than 1.5% of the energy falls below 5 μm. The energy from a body at 300 K (or 27 °C) peaks at 9.6 μm and has 38% of its energy in the 8–14 μm band. This is rather fortunate, in that the atmosphere has another transmission window from 8–14 μm.

The rationale for the choice of bands has two components: first, the peak wavelength of the source of illumination; and second, the location of the atmospheric transmission windows. For visual systems the source of the illumination is the sun, and therefore this band is centered at 0.55 μm extending from 0.4 μm to 0.75 μm. In the IR bands the source of radiation is primarily the object itself. For aircraft the more appropriate band is the 3–5 μm band dictated by an atmospheric

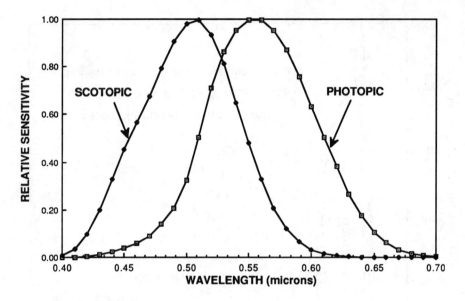

Figure 2.3 Spectral sensitivity of the human eye.

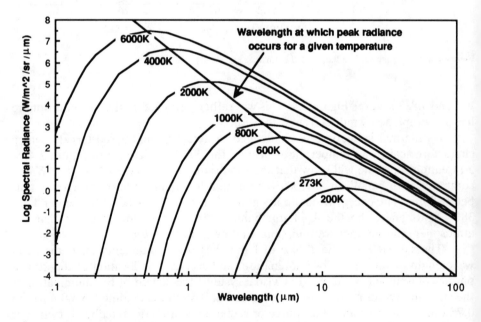

Figure 2.4 Blackbody spectral radiance at several temperatures.

window. For ground-based objects at nearer 300 K the wavelength for peak radiation is at 10 μm, which is straddled by another atmospheric window extending from 8 μm to 12 μm. This is not meant to imply that for ground-based objects we might not use the 3–5 μm band; it merely points out that objects give peak radiation at the longer wavelengths. The question of which band sensor to use in a given scenario is reserved for later chapters on total system analysis.

One final comment is needed with regard to windows. The term is misleading in that it implies very high transmission. When dealing with the atmosphere in the "pass bands" that we have discussed as windows the absorption and scattering are far from negligible. This will be discussed in detail in Chapter 5, which is concerned with atmospherics.

2.1.2 Resolution

While dealing with the issue of wavelength one of the most useful formulas for a first test of any practical optical system is to establish the limiting resolution of that system. Assuming that the system is diffraction limited, then the size of the blur circle is given in radians as

$$\theta = 2.44\,\lambda/D \tag{2.2}$$

where

λ = wavelength (m)
D = diameter of the optics (m).

Whether creating a new system or checking an existing one this simple formula is perhaps the most useful starting point. The diameter D in reality is the effective aperture and will in general be smaller than the physical aperture; however, for well-designed optics and for a first-order approximation, they may be treated as identical. For comparing the effect of wavelength on the size of the aperture, Figure 2.5 is useful. The figure provides a graph of effective aperture required for a given resolution for the three center wavelengths considered in this book: 0.55 μm, 4 μm, and 10 μm.

It is interesting to note that, in spite of all the favorable reasons (light level, smoke penetration, *et cetera*) for selecting wavelengths longer than the visible, there is a cost in size and therefore weight attributed to the aperture requirements of these longer wavelengths for a given resolution. For a fixed resolution requirement the aperture for an 8–12 μm sensor is in direct proportion to the wavelength for a visible band sensor; that is, some 18:1 ratio. We shall see later that resolution and sensitivity dictate the ability to detect, recognize, and classify objects. The

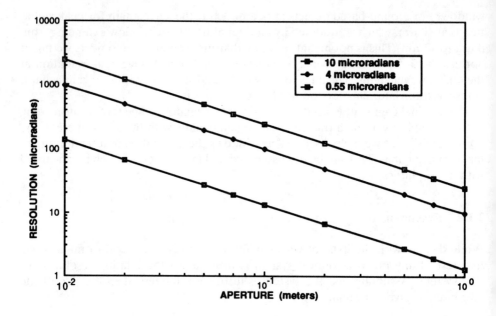

Figure 2.5 Optical system resolution *versus* effective aperture.

infrared bands usually yield higher sensitivities. There is therefore a conscious decision by the designer to trade off resolution against sensitivity at the longer wavelengths to achieve the performance requirements.

2.2 TV SENSORS

The basic TV sensor has been with us for many decades but its exploitation has been principally in the commercial sector. Every house in the United States has a TV set that receives pictures broadcasted from a TV camera operating in some remote studio. The basic sensor did not start to be readily applied to military systems until the 1950s, primarily due to its lack of robustness and secondarily because it was quite bulky. This changed primarily due to some severe system-driving issues. TV first found its way onto tracking, fire control platforms, which were principally large radar tracking platforms. Their large size meant that the TV cameras (large by today's standard) had little impact on platform characteristics. Radar tracking platforms suffered from multipath effects while tracking targets at low altitude. The effect caused the platform to oscillate violently and lose the track. The augmentation of the radar by a TV tracking system circumvented this problem. These early platforms were so successful that entirely electro-optical fire control directors were developed. Removing the expensive radar led to a less expensive fire control pedestal and a totally passive tracking system. Such electro-optical systems have been used quite successfully for such applications as fire directors for fast patrol boats. They are particularly useful where the weapon they are directing, such as a 25 mm or 30 mm gun, is of only very limited range capability. The added extended range (>40 km) capability of a tracking radar provides no real benefit to the accuracy of the final engagement.

As cameras developed in ruggedness, they were applied to such platforms as tanks. Here the advantage they initially offered over direct vision systems was a reduction in the size of the hole in the armor to accommodate the system. It also offered the opportunity to "pipe" the outside scene to both commander and gunner within the tank instead of using hard optic relays. The TV in this arena is still not considered totally as a replacement for hard optics because of reliability issues and the remoting effects of the environment from the crew. We may see a resurgence of activity in this arena, however, as the impact of laser safety on direct view optics on the battlefield finds its way into specifications. A secondary resurgence for replacing direct view optics will also come as more automatic target cuers and recognizers are added to main battle tanks.

As cameras reduced in size, we started to see shells and missiles carrying TV cameras. The most recent example of this is the FOG-M (fiber optic-guided missile), which carries a TV sensor in its nose. TV sensors over the last 40 or 50 years have played a significant role in military target acquisition.

With the explosion of interest in the 1960s and 1970s in FLIRs, the interest in military applications for TV systems all but disappeared. Many of the arguments used to favor FLIR systems over TV systems though are not necessarily as black and white when held up to cold scientific investigation. The inability of TV systems to see through fog, smoke, and dust is an evident limitation when compared to a FLIR, until one measures the actual range advantage afforded by a FLIR and the system cost incurred. The inability of systems working in the visible spectrum to see at night too has been negated by the advent of second- and third-generation image intensifier tubes. These microchannel plate-image intensifiers have been coupled to TV camera tubes to give performance comparable to FLIR systems at less cost with a more reliable field performance: the weakness in the FLIR system always seems to rest with the cryogenics.

We will dwell later on image intensifiers. For now we will deal primarily with the discussion of three common television sensors: the vidicon tube, the charged coupled device, and the charge injection device. The television camera tube is an electronic device that converts an optical image into an electrical signal. Camera tubes are used to generate a train of electrical pulses, which represent light intensities present in an optical image focused on the tube.

The vidicon is the most widely used camera tube. Its small size and simplicity of operation and adjustment permit its use by relatively inexperienced personnel. Vidicons have moderate sensitivity and can be used in many locations. The speed of response of the vidicon is generally somewhat less than that of most other types of cameras.

The most basic vidicon consists of a scanning electron beam and a charged photoconductive target. This photoconductive target is the light sensor. Its front side forms the positively charged electrode (cathode), which is covered with a transparent conductive layer. The back of the target is the anode, which is maintained near zero potential. Light patterns from an observed scene are focused on the photoconductor. These increase the conductivity as a function of light level and cause the anode to approach the potential of the cathode. As an electron beam scans the back of the photoconductor it deposits electrons on the positively charged anode. The more positive the charge, the more electrons it deposits. The beam current effectively reads the illumination deposited on the front side of the photoconductor. This remarkably simple device has been produced by various TV tube manufacturing companies, each with its own version of this basic vidicon design under such different tradenames as Epicon (General Electric), Plumbicon (Phillips), Sidicon (English Electric), and ST-Vidicon (RCA). In general these tubes differ by the different types of target materials, with lead oxide and silicon being the dominant choices.

In addition to the vidicons, one encounters a few more exotic tubes. For higher sensitivity, lower light levels, there are image orthicons, image isocons, *silicon intensified target* (SIT), and *secondary electron conduction* (SEC) tubes. In choosing tubes for military applications the major trade-off parameters are resolution, signal-to-noise ratio, third-field lag, faceplate illuminance, dynamic range, MTF, and ruggedness.

During the last few years we have seen conventional tube TV systems replaced by *charge coupled device* (CCD) and *charge injection device* (CID) solid-state TV systems. In a drive that owes more to a perception of all solid states being more reliable than is borne out by reality, there has been an irrational rejection of conventional tube designs. This was evident even in the early days when the dynamic range of a CCD was very limited. It had poor resolution and poor sensitivity, yet could be damaged by direct sunlight. Finally early CCD arrays bloomed and bled badly. Today's CCD devices are much better. They have sensitivities and resolutions comparable to the vidicons. However, they are still not as rugged thermally as one would desire for military applications. The main advantage of a CCD is that it requires no scanning beam. The device consists of a two-dimensional array of photosensitive elements. Each of these elements converts incident illumination to a proportional electric charge that it stores on its individual *metal oxide silicon* (MOS) capacitor. The stored charge represents the illumination on each picture element. A multiphase clocking operation applies a positive charge to adjacent electrodes which in turn transfers the charge sequentially across the MOS capacitors. In this manner the charges appear sequentially at an output gate located at the edge of the detector.

This fundamental simplicity of operation provides the CCD with some of its major original operational problems. If the illumination is too strong, the stored potential wells under the depletion-biased electrodes overflow and spill into its adjoining neighbors. The result is known as *blooming*.

The CID is a contemporary device of the CCD. It is a similar two-dimensional array of photosensitive material; however, it avoids the limitations of the CCD by measuring directly the charge stored under each element without shifting or disturbing that charge. The charge is isolated from adjacent charges, and hence no spillover can occur. The CID TV sensor therefore has all the advantages of the CCD—compactness, resolution, and ruggedness—with the addition of antiblooming and antistreaking characteristics. CID sensors are available today in 4:3 aspect ratio with array sizes of 776 (H) × 512 (V).

During the last decade, we have seen bigger and bigger arrays and a tendency for the majority of these to be color CCD cameras. Commercially available in your local video store are hand-held CCD cameras weighing around 2 pounds with color CCD chips or arrays of over 400,000 pixels on a one-half inch chip.

As stated earlier it is not possible always to have good illumination. During the day the illuminance afforded by the sun can range from a few hundred lux to 10^5 lux. With the faceplate sensitivity of vidicons, CCD, and CIDS, even in the face of high F number optics there are sufficient photons for full performance of these systems. However, as the sun sets so the illuminance drops rapidly from 10^{-1} lux to 10^{-3} (clear night sky) to even 10^{-4} lux (overcast night sky). At these light levels, vidicons fail to operate below about 10^{-2} lux faceplate illuminance, and although SITs will work down to 10^{-4} lux faceplate illuminance, the signal-to-noise ratio is poor and the third-field lag is extreme. The solution is to use a second- or third-generation image intensifier to act as a photon multiplier. These high-gain photon stages can be optically coupled directly to a vidicon or to a CCD stage to provide a low light level camera. Care must be used in matching camera and intensifier to maintain a reasonable MTF of the total system. To turn a low light level TV camera into an all light camera, all that is required is sophisticated closed loop control of *light level* (LL), *automatic light control* (ALC), and *automatic gain control* (AGC).

2.3 TELESCOPIC SIGHT

A telescopic sight is the simplest of the systems considered in this book. In this system the image is never converted into an electronic signal, but instead is transferred using only optics. As shown in Figure 2.6 the objective optics produce a real image of a distant scene. The eyepiece produces the displayed image, which is virtual, also very distant, and generally enlarged. In effect, the eyepiece is used as a simple magnifier, or magnifying glass, to examine the real image from the

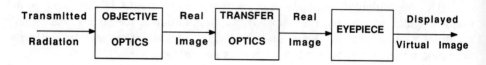

Figure 2.6 Block diagram of telescopic sight or direct view optics.

objective. There may be additional optics between the objective and the eyepiece to change the image orientation or to move it to a more convenient location or reduce vignetting, but the essence of a telescopic sight is composed of just these two components.

Compared to the naked eye, telescopic sights, which include binoculars, provide the advantage of magnification at the expense of a restricted field of view, some loss in luminance and resolution, and a slower search. The system analyst must decide whether the gain in the one area overrides the loss in the others for the particular application at hand. For example, Figure 2.7 shows a graph of detection probability *versus* range for the naked eye and 7 × 35 binoculars in a 30 s search of 20° × 5° for a 3 m × 3 m target of 8% reflectance against a 10% reflectance background in full daylight with 12 km visibility. The interesting feature in this graph is that the curves cross: at ranges below ≈1.5 km it is better to search by eye, but at longer ranges the binoculars are better. This result is obtained because

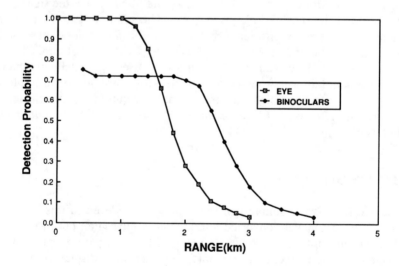

Figure 2.7 Performance of the eye, unaided and with 7 × 35 binoculars: 3 m^2 target of 8% reflectance against 10% background in full daylight, 12 km visibility. 30 s search of 20° × 5°.

at shorter ranges magnification is not needed to detect this size target, but it does slow down the search as the area without a target is also magnified and must be searched. At longer ranges, magnification still slows down the search but it becomes necessary to make detection feasible when one looks at the target. The crossover range will depend on search sector, search time, visibility, target size, magnification, and so forth so there is no general answer to the question of whether a telescopic sight is better than the naked eye: it depends on the circumstances of the problem. What is clear is that search must somehow be modeled to arrive at a reasonable answer because higher magnification always outperforms lower if it is first assumed that the observer is already looking directly at the target. This consideration will be dealt with later, in the chapter on human modeling.

2.4 IR SENSING SYSTEMS

For over 50 years humankind has put its mind to sensing infrared radiation from the earliest continuous film devices to the modern detector arrays. It is worth noting that IR systems were being developed at the same time as the early radars. In *The Wizard Wars*, R. V. Jones ("the man of the beams") points out that he was working on an IR detector just prior to the start of World War II. Early radar and IR developments ran parallel, however, a decision to put the majority of military technology resources available at that time in a race to complete one technology left radar with a huge lead in technical maturity at the end of the war. Following this there was a relatively slow adoption by the military, which caused the lag in the development of IR technology. Recently there has been a growing move by the military toward passive systems. As a result, IR technology is going through a period of rapid growth.

The first thermal imaging system developed was the circa 1930 Evaporagraph. It was a relatively insensitive nonscanning device. By the late 1930s and early 1940s, two alternative approaches were evident. One was to develop discrete detectors, mechanically scanned analogous to TV systems. The other was to develop infrared vidicons. Originally, scanning thermal imagers were called *thermographs*. They were single-detector elements that had two-dimensional, slow framing scanners. They recorded their images on photographic materials. In 1952, the Army built the first thermograph using a 16-inch searchlight reflector, a dual axis scanner, and a bolometer detector. Up to then development of a fast framing imager was infeasible because of the lack of availability of detectors with sufficient sensitivity with fast response times. Electrical signal bandwidths had to be limited to a few hundred hertz because poor detector response above this range gave low signal-to-noise ratios (SNR). The development of cooled short time constant indium antimonide (In Sb) and mercury-doped germanium (Ge:Hg) photoconductive detectors made possible the first fast framing sensors.

The first FLIR sensor was an outgrowth of a downward looking strip mapper. In the 1960s the uniform FLIR (after a few false starts) was resurrected by the U.S. Air Force (a TI FLIR) and the U.S. Navy (a Hughes FLIR). From 1960 to 1974 no less than 60 different FLIRs were developed.

FLIR technology reached maturity in the late 1970s and early 1980s with the development of HgCdTe detector arrays, which perform at near theoretical thermal sensitivity limits while providing signal responses fast enough to sustain the wider bandwidth necessary for the high ratios of field of view to resolution requirements. Compact and efficient cryogenic coolers and detector devices are the future of FLIRs together with advancements in electronic signal processing.

2.4.1 Basic FLIR Descriptions

The term *forward looking infrared* was first used in airborne applications to distinguish it as an imaging system as distinct from the downward looking single channel thermal mapping system and from single framing thermographic cameras. FLIR is used nowadays to denote any fast framing (e.g., 30 Hz frame time or faster) thermal imager.

A FLIR consists of an optical system that collects, spectrally filters, and focuses the infrared radiation (see Figure 2.8). For a serial scanned, standard video FLIR system, such as shown in Figure 2.8, the received infrared radiation is scanned horizontally and vertically, which in turn directs the received radiation from a patch in object space onto the detector. Another way to explain the operation is to start at the detector and look back through the scanning process to the projection of the detector in object space. As the scanning continues so the detector's projection proceeds to scan the field of view. This scanning procedure describes generically the class of the FLIR. The detector, which is usually cryogenically cooled, converts the received radiance to an electrical signal. That signal in turn is converted into a standard TV format, whereupon it can be fed to a display monitor for operator interpretation.

This FLIR description describes the particular class of serial scanned, standard video FLIRs; however it is sufficiently general that most of the other classes can be derived or inferred from a little understanding of detectors and scanning mechanisms. If one only has a single or a small number of discrete detectors, one is restricted to a serial scanned process. If one can fill a whole column with detectors, then one requires only scanning that column of detectors across the field-of-view, as illustrated in Figure 2.9. This is known as a *parallel scan FLIR*. If one has a full, two-dimensional array of detectors, as also shown in Figure 2.9, one can remove the scanning mechanism completely. This is known as a *staring array*. To understand the implications from a FLIR sensitivity aspect it is necessary to realize that the output of the detector to infrared radiation falling upon it is proportional

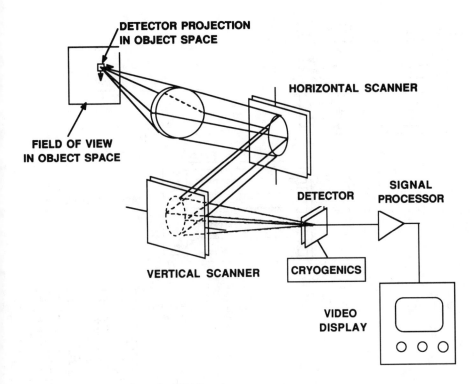

DETECTOR PROJECTION IN OBJECT SPACE

HORIZONTAL SCANNER

FIELD OF VIEW IN OBJECT SPACE

SIGNAL PROCESSOR

DETECTOR

VERTICAL SCANNER

CRYOGENICS

VIDEO DISPLAY

Figure 2.8 Components of a typical FLIR system.

to the integration time (or the time the detector is allowed to dwell on that radiation patch). For a single element to scan the field of view at the U.S. standard field rate of 30 Hz or the U.K. equivalent of 25 Hz, with 512 resolvable elements in both the horizontal and vertical axes, the maximum allowable dwell time in one resolution cell is on the order of .1 μs. Fortunately the industry has not been limited to single detectors; it built arrays. In the early days in the United States arrays of 14 discrete element detectors were used. By serial scanning the scene each detector sequentially visited the same region in object space. By time delaying the output of each detector and integrating these outputs a gain in signal-to-noise ratio, and hence, sensitivity was achieved. This process is known as *time delay integration* (TDI).

Instead of having a series of discrete detectors whose output was individually summed, the United Kingdom took the very innovative step of laying down a long bar of detector material and, through appropriate biasing, obtained essentially the same time delay and integration within the detector itself. The device, known as *SPRITE* (which will be described later), allowed the full advantages of a serial

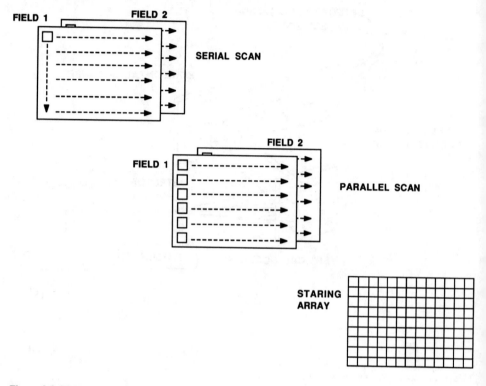

Figure 2.9 FLIR image dissection types.

scan system (with very few disadvantages) and was used on both sides of the Atlantic.

The thrust within the United States at that time was to make long, linear arrays of detectors. The FLIRs that resulted obtained their sensitivity by the increased dwell afforded by parallel scan devices. Because each detector now had to travel only the width of the field of view, for the same horizontal resolution of the example chosen earlier, the dwell time would be on the order of 50 μs (or a 500:1 improvement in integration time).

Of all the elements in a FLIR system (see Figure 2.10) by far the most expensive part is the detector-dewar. For this reason, when designing a FLIR for a given application, one chooses a basic FLIR that uses, say, either the U.S. common module detector-dewar, or, the U.K. SPRITE detector (discussed later) and then tailors the design by modifying the optics rather than designing a new detector. Typical performance specifications for the U.S. common module detector-dewar are given in Table 2.2.

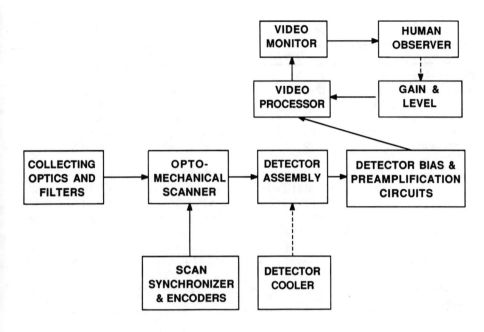

Figure 2.10 Block diagram of a typical FLIR system.

All FLIRs use their properties of thermal sensitivity, image sharpness, spectral response, dynamic range, contrast rendition, and magnification to produce a visual facsimile of a thermal scene. We will discuss briefly a few of these sensors: a serial scanned, standard video; a parallel scanned, parallel video system; a parallel scanned, standard video system; and a staring array.

2.4.1.1 Serial Scanned, Standard Video Devices

Serial scanned, standard video devices are very common and represent the norms of the industry. These systems differ in their scanning procedure, their use of discrete element detectors versus continuous bar detectors (e.g., SPRITE), and in their use of vertical and horizontal time delay and integration; see Figure 2.11.

There are all sorts of variations of TDI on the serial scanned device from an array of a small number of discrete elements (14 seems to be a common number) with horizontal TDI and either 1 bar of these elements or 2, 4, or 8 bars providing horizontal TDI through to 4 or 8 bar SPRITE detectors. Time delay and integration provides the property of enhancing the SNR over a single detector by the square root of the number of detectors, the premise being that the signal is coherent and

Table 2.2
IR Common Module Characteristics

	MIL-D-49446	MIL-D-49457	MIL-D-49172
Number of elements	60	120	180
Blackbody detectivity ($\times 10^9$ cm/$\sqrt{\text{Hz}}$/W)	Ctr 12 < 9.0 Min > 7.5	Avg > 11.0 Min > 8.5 Soft > 5.0	Avg > 11.0 Min > 8.5 Soft > 5.0
Blackbody responsivity (V/W)	8 k < $\mathscr{R}_{bb}$ < 20 k ± 20%	8.3 k < $\mathscr{R}_{bb}$ < 20 k ± 20%	8.3 k < $\mathscr{R}_{bb}$ < 20 k ± 20%
Microphonics	<10 dB between 50 Hz–20 kHz with 50 Hz BW	<10 dB between 50 Hz–20 kHz with 50 Hz BW	<10 dB between 50 Hz–20 kHz with 50 Hz BW
Detector bias (mA)	Avg < 3.0 All < 6.0 + 3.0 ± 0.2 Vdc	All < 4.0 + 5.0 ± 0.2 Vdc	All < 4.0 + 5.0 ± 0.2 Vdc
Heat load at full bias (W)	< 0.12 at 80 ± 5 K	< 0.37 at 80 ± 5 K	< 0.40 at 80 ± 5 K
Spectral response (μm)	7.7 ± 0.3 to 11.7 ± 0.5	7.7 ± 0.3 to 11.7 ± 0.5	7.7 ± 0.3 to 11.7 ± 0.5

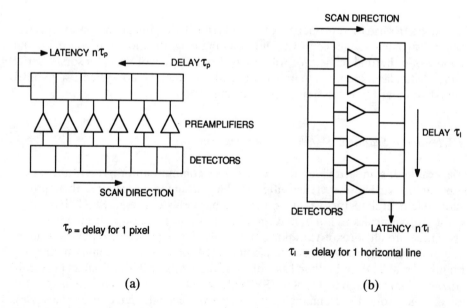

(a)

(b)

Figure 2.11 Horizontal (a) and vertical (b) time delay and integration.

therefore the signal voltage adds coherently, whereas the noise is uncorrelated and therefore adds as the square root of the sum of the squares of an individual detector. The U.K. SPRITE (signal processing in the element) effectively forms a similar TDI in a long bar of a detector material, by matching the physical scan rate to the migration rate of electrons across the detector. The latter is achieved by imposing a dc potential across the element. This detector will be discussed later in the chapter.

The principal advantage of this serial scan technique is that one detector (or one set of detectors) views every picture element within the scene, and therefore there is no need to balance the responsivity of each detector. The detectors can be made as responsive as possible without undue regard to uniformity. The disadvantage is that now a two-axis scanner has to be provided.

Its operation is fairly straightforward. A two-axis scanner is slaved to a TV sync generator that provides a TV-like raster scan. Essentially this scanner projects the detector in object space. The detector converts the IR energy received from the scene into video, which is processed (i.e., time delayed and integrated, AC coupled, gain and level set) and sends RS 170 (or some other common video format) to a display. Other video standards such as the European CCIR 625B standards can be selected by changing the TV sync generator. Europeans use a 625-line system whereas the United States uses a 525-line system.

Of the inherent advantages of serial scanned FLIRs, perhaps the strongest is the picture uniformity afforded by having only a few channels (namely 1, 4, or 8 at maximum). This allows detectors to be optimized to yield highest sensitivity, or D^*, without compromised uniformity. The design allows direct RS-170 compatibility without reformatting (or scan conversion), which leads to very compact systems. Finally, the design yields minimal video delays and therefore minimal distortion under slew conditions. This is somewhat offset by the short integration time per pixel and the large bandwidth (typically 4–5 MHz) required of the detector.

2.4.1.2 *Parallel Scanned, Parallel Video System*

One of the smallest, simplest, and cheapest thermal imagers is the parallel scan, parallel video system (such as an AN/TAS-4) that uses detectors individually connected to LEDs and one mirror that both scans the scene across the detector array and scans the LED array across the observer's field of view. The disadvantage of a parallel video system is that only one observer looking through the eyepiece sees the display at any time.

A simplified diagrammatic representation of the AN/TAS-4 (a parallel scanned, parallel video device) is shown in Figure 2.12. Its operation is described as follows. An afocal telescope receives IR energy and determines the field of view and optical magnification of the IR system. The mechanical scanner houses the scan mirror, which pivots about the vertical scan axis. This mirror scans the scene

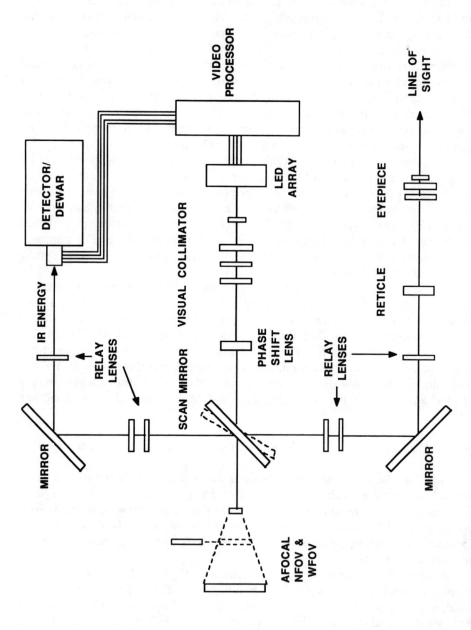

Figure 2.12 Simplified diagram of AN/TAS-4 FLIR.

horizontally across the vertical detector array. Another mirror oscillates about the interlace axis at 60 Hz to form a 2:1 interlaced scan. The array of detectors within the detector-dewar assembly converts the received IR energy to video signals that are amplified and used to drive the emitters in an array of LEDs. There is a 1:1 matching of LEDs to IR detectors. The light emitted from the LEDs is optically returned to the back of the scanning mirror, which therefore synchronously scans the visual image on the reticle with the received IR energy from the scene. The AN/TAS-4 contains all the necessary brightness, level, and contrast control to adjust the video signal to the LED array. The detector array consists of a discrete 60 active-element linear array of HgCdTe (mercury-cadmium-telluride) photoconductive detectors.

2.4.1.3 Parallel Scanned, Standard Video Devices

The common module parallel scanned, standard video FLIRs have little difference diagrammatically to the parallel scanned, parallel video FLIRs from the lens through to the detector-dewar assembly. The difference comes after this stage. The electrical output from the detector instead of being amplified to drive a LED is stored and scan converted into a standard RS-170 (or equivalent) format. This is in turn used to drive a monitor.

Parallel scanned, standard video FLIRs have been the backbone of the U.S. military FLIR business throughout the 1970s and 1980s. Initial systems were made from 60-element common module arrays, but gradually higher-performance systems evolved using arrays of 120 and 180 elements. Today common module systems such as LANTIRN (low altitude navigation targeting infrared system), manufactured by Martin Marietta, offers the pilot an infrared image with the highest quality resolution and sensitivity.

The advantage of the parallel scanned FLIR over its serial scanned counterpart is the increased dwell time of the detector and the corresponding reduction in bandwidth requirements to around 40–50 kHz. The disadvantage is one of uniformity. To ensure a uniform picture, disparities in sensitivity of individual detectors have to be corrected electronically. To have reasonably uniform arrays the penalty is a relaxation in peak detectivity.

2.4.1.4 Staring Arrays

As detector arrays became larger (i.e., 512 × 512) and more uniform the scanning mechanism could be dropped from the assembly. Each detector could be used to stare at its particular part of the scene. Each detector is refreshed at 1/60 second, and so it has a long dwell time, thereby increasing its sensitivity. Today large arrays made of platinum silicide are available in the 3–5 μm bands. Indium antimonide,

InSb, staring systems are commercially available. Large arrays in HgCdTe covering the 8–12 μm band are yet to be available, however, 256 × 256 arrays are available for laboratory prototypes.

In spite of the advantage of longer dwell times, the big disadvantage of this technology is the added complexity of uniformity compensation and the necessity for scan conversion. The lack of array uniformity has held up the development of HgCdTe staring arrays. In the United States, we believe, arrays of 128 × 128 are available from Hughes, Amber, and Cincinnati electronics. In the United Kingdom similar size arrays are available through Phillips (Mullard) and GEC.

2.4.2 Current Tactical Imaging Systems

Much emphasis is given in infrared research to IR detectors and the development trends in detector technology. However, of real importance to the system user is the total imaging system. The ideal thermal imager is one in which the IR emitted from the scene is imaged onto a surface (preferably uncooled) where it is converted into a visible picture.

The thrust within the United States and the United Kingdom is to develop uncooled imagers that equal or surpass many of today's cooled imagers. Texas Instruments, under a DOD contract, is developing an uncooled ferroelectric staring array; and Honeywell is developing a microbolometric array. As can be seen by Table 2.3 both devices have over 100,000 elements, totally staring, and aimed at achieving system noise-equivalent temperature differences of around 0.1 °C. Similar performances are being projected in the United Kingdom from pyroelectric detectors using modified lead zirconate by GEC-Marconi Materials Technology. What is interesting to note is that with this projected noise-equivalent temperature difference, and a dynamic range of at least 80 dB, these uncooled systems will provide performance in excess of what is required for many of our present fielded systems.

Table 2.3
Tactical Imaging Systems

FPA Type	Hybrid	Monolithic
Material	Strontium barium titanate	Micromachined silicon
Detection mechanism	Ferroelectric dielectric constant change, enhanced by Curie point	Bolometric resistance change, pulse-biased readout
Crosstalk demonstrated	5%	0.1% or less
NETD in lab	0.13 °C (0.2 °C practical)	0.1 °C (0.2 °C practical)
Array size	245 × 328	240 × 336

2.4.3 FLIR Components

In the earlier part of this chapter all the emphasis was given to the overall FLIR; however, it is evident that the FLIR design is dictated by four major components: the afocal telescope, the scanner mechanism, the detector-dewar, and the cryogenic source. The afocal telescope stage forms a key part of any design and tailors the FLIR optically for its application. This stage provides the required resolution and fields of view for the task at hand. When adapting an existing FLIR for a new application, this optical stage is by far the easiest element to modify. Care must be taken to ensure that the afocal stage is athermalized (especially in the 8–12 μm band) and that all MTF characteristics are met.

Scanning mechanisms are usually mirrors, although, if nondiffraction limited performance is acceptable, refractive optics may be used. The advantage of the latter is the possibility to generate a rather complex piece of refractive optics that scans both elevation and azimuth axis simultaneously, thereby avoiding the difficult problem of having to continuously synchronize independent azimuth and elevation scanning mirrors as in the more usual case. There is no desire to dwell much longer on scanning mechanisms as they will soon be components of the past. The need for scanners is intrinsic to the limitations of previous detector arrays. As detector arrays become two-dimensional, high-resolution arrays, so the need for scanners becomes obsolete.

The most expensive part of any new FLIR design is the detector-dewar. It is the heart of all FLIRs and as such dictates the capabilities, limitations, and future trends of FLIRs. In view of its significance, the next section is dedicated to an overview of detector technology.

The last FLIR component of significance is the cryogenic stage. Unfortunately, to date this has proved the Achilles heel of FLIRs. Cryogenic stages have a history of being unreliable, and the source of induced noise and vibration into assemblies and platforms. They contribute considerably to the weight of any FLIR and correspondingly to the size. Although cryogenic stages continue to improve, it is anticipated that detector technology's drive for the uncooled array will eventually obviate the need for cryogenics before all the mechanical problems of this stage are resolved.

2.4.3.1 *Cryogenics*

At present the only practical method of providing high-quality real-time imagery is by the use of imaging systems employing arrays of cooled quantum detectors coupled with mechanical scanning devices. This solution departs from the ideal in many areas; most noticeable, however, is that the device has to be cooled and that the array has to be mechanically scanned. When we look at the requirements for military systems: (1) maximum performance; (2) smallest, lightest package; (3) low power consumption; (4) low cost; and (5) high reliability, the shortcomings of the present technology are evident. Maximum performance is achieved by cooling the detector. The cryogenics are the big stumbling block in modern systems. Although advances continue in this area, reliability is poor, typically on the order of a few hundred hours before failure, and the cheaper, lighter systems need a constantly replenished coolant supply. This creates a logistic problem. Cooling systems (cryogenics) are a technology in their own right and for IR detectors operating at around 80 K a list of advantages and disadvantages are given in Table 2.4.

There are basically two types of coolers; integral coolers and split coolers. With integral coolers the whole cooler is fixed to the detector-dewar, which not only restricts the designer in terms of packaging but also has the other disadvantage of transmitting cooler vibrations directly into the detector-dewars. The split cycle cooler separates the cooler body from the cold finger (i.e., the detector-dewar) with a formable transfer line. The result is to give the packaging engineer a more flexible design environment and, further, isolates the detector from the cooler-induced vibration. Split cycle coolers today have linear as well as rotary compressor designs. The linear designs can be single or dual piston.

The more popular cooling systems for IR detectors at 77 K are the single-piston split linear cycle Stirling engines. The trend is away from rotary engines more toward the linear in-line compressor. The result has been more efficient, smaller, and lighter cooling systems, which generate less noise and vibration. Vibration is of serious concern to lightweight stabilization systems that use FLIRs as one of the target acquisition devices. The high-frequency vibration is transmitted directly to the platform and, without extreme care, will cause the line of sight to vibrate, thereby degrading the overall modulation transfer function of the optical system. The penalty of added inertia and self-induced vibration is so large with some high-performance, stabilized, IR target acquisition systems that designers go to inordinate amounts of complexity to off-load and isolate the cryogenic source from the FLIR-carrying gimbal. Designers wait for the day when today's FLIR

Table 2.4
Cooling Systems for IR Detectors at 80 K

System	Advantages	Disadvantages
Liedenfrost	Cheapest, simple	Logistic problems
Liquid transfer	Silent, light, compact at detector	Evaporative loss at all times
Joule-Thomson	Cheaper than engine, silent, compact	Bulk and weight of gas bottle, logistic problems
Engine	Efficient, light, compact	Expensive, vibration, acoustic noise

performance can be achieved at temperatures of 173 K or above, when solid state Peltier coolers can be used. The result will be smaller, lighter FLIRs with no vibration-inducing components.

2.4.3.2 Detectors

Over the last 50 years detectors have come an amazingly long way from the earliest oil film deformation (evaporagraphic) devices, through IR vidicon tubes (both semiconductor and pyroelectric), to today's two-dimensional second-generation focal plane arrays. The earlier devices take their respective place in history but are so obsolete that no book of this nature should dwell at any length on them.

In general there are two main classes of IR detectors, thermal and photon, as shown in Table 2.5. Although photon detectors are of most interest from a military standpoint, we will use thermal detectors to introduce some of the concepts of performance measure with a detector.

Table 2.5
Infrared Detectors

Thermal Detectors	Photon Detectors
Bolometer	Photoconductive
Thermocouples	Block impurity band
Thermopiles	Quantum well
Thermopneumatic	Photovoltaic
Pyroelectric	Photoemissive
	Schottky barrier
Ferroelectric	Metal insulator semiconductor

A thermal detector measures the change in temperature that results in absorbed and emitted streams of photons, whose arrival and departure rates fluctuate randomly. This randomness causes a fluctuation in arrival of photons at the detector and hence its output signal. The mean square fluctuation in radiant power is given by

$$\Delta \phi^2 = 16 A_d k \sigma \epsilon T_d^2 \Delta f \tag{2.3}$$

where

A_d = detector area
k = Boltzmann's constant
σ = Stefan-Boltzmann constant
ϵ = emissivity

T_d = detector temperature in Kelvins
Δf = electrical bandwidth.

Without considering other sources of noise, such as Johnson noise, (2.3) yields the noise equivalent power limitation of a thermal device. What is evident is the critical need to lower the temperature of the detector to lower its noise equivalent power.

As stated earlier, of interest to the military electro-optical systems analyst is the photon detector. The list of photon detectors in Table 2.5 is given for completeness, however, here we will dwell on only photoconductive and photovoltaic devices. A photoconductive device increases its conductivity when incident infrared photons are absorbed by the detector. This results in free-charge carriers being produced by the absorption of the photons. In any electrical circuit the change in conductivity (i.e., a decrease in resistance) results in an increase in signal current.

A photovoltaic detector on the other hand is a *p-n* junction on a semiconductor. Infrared photons absorbed at or near the junction produce conduction electrons that in turn produce an external current. This current, which is related to the number of incident photons, is isolated by the junction.

The voltage output of a detector contains noise from internal sources, as well as being subjected to the noise (or random fluctuation) inherent in the incident radiation. The internal noise may be classified as generation-recombination noise, current or $1/f$ noise, Johnson noise, or shot noise. All noise sources are related to temperature. Johnson noise is a direct function of detector temperature, the remainder as a function of detector resistance that in turn is related to temperatures. Cooling the detector therefore reduces noise effects. Cooling is achieved by using the dewar attached to the cryogenic source.

As the signal derived from a detector is mixed with noise, a limitation on the performance of the device occurs when the signal power equates to the noise power. As stated earlier there are four main sources of internal noise (excluding preamp noise) and an exterior source of noise (photon noise). The vector summation of these noise sources forms a figure of merit of a detector, and that is expressed as the minimum temperature difference it can detect. We will look at these noise sources individually.

Johnson noise is associated with the electrical resistance of the detector and is expressed as

$$V_{\text{nrms}} = \sqrt{4kTR\Delta f} \tag{2.4}$$

where

R = resistance (ohms)
Δf = noise equivalent power bandwidth (Hz).

Shot noise results from random electrons in electronic circuit and is expressed by

$$I_{\text{nrms}} = \sqrt{2eI\Delta f} \qquad (2.5)$$

where

e = electron charge
I = total current.

Generation-recombination noise is caused by random generation and recombination of charge carriers in a semiconductor and is expressed as

$$V_{\text{nrms}} = \overline{R}I\left[\frac{2\tau\Delta f}{4(1 + 4n^2 f^2 \tau^2)}\right]^{1/2} \qquad (2.6)$$

where

$\overline{R}$ = static resistance
I = dc current
τ = carrier lifetime
n = carrier density.

Excess noise is sometimes called *flicker noise* and is inversely proportional to some power of frequency. This may be expressed by

$$I_{\text{nrms}} = KI^2/f^a \qquad (2.7)$$

where

K = a constant
I = dc current
f = frequency
a = variable.

Photon noise is caused by the random arrival rate of the photons at the detector similar to that described by (2.3). This is expressed as

$$\Delta n_{\text{rms}} = \sqrt{n} \qquad (2.8)$$

where n is the average number of photons per unit of time.

If all the internal noise could be reduced to 0, the limiting performance would be determined by the fluctuations in the rate of arrival of incident photons. This is called *background limited performance* (BLIP). The mean square fluctuation in the rate of arrival is a function of both the wavelength and the temperature of the observed scene. The actual scene temperature is beyond the control of the designer, however, one can limit how much of the scene is observed (by reducing the cone angle of the cold shield). Reducing cone angle therefore reduces photon noise. Photon noise can be further reduced by spectral filtering, although it is better to use this technique to enhance contrast by spectrally filtering the target with respect to the background.

A photoconductor at equilibrium has a total noise power that can be no less than twice the photon noise power. This means that the detectivity (proportional to noise equivalent power) for an ideal photoconductor is less than (i.e., more sensitive) than that for an ideal photovoltaic detector by a factor of 2.

To turn the discussion to a more practical side, the big breakthroughs in the proliferation of FLIRs were caused by two detector arrays. One of these was the U.S. common module detector and the other was the U.K. SPRITE (signal processing in the element) detector.

The common module detector is a vertical column of 60, 120, or 180 mercury cadmium telluride (HgCdTe) detectors. Each detector is individually wired to its preamplifier. A vertical column of, say, 120 detectors can be scanned horizontally in one field, shifted by half a line separation, and scanned in the next field to form a frame with a 240-vertical-frame resolution. Doubling the number of detectors doubles the line resolution.

The U.K. SPRITE detector, also a *mercury cadmium telluride* (MCT) device, works in a considerably different manner. The SPRITE was a concept of C. T. Elliott of the Royal Signals and Radar Establishment, Malvern, U.K. Instead of an individual detector, the detector is made much larger than the instantaneous field of view. This strip of infrared-sensitive material is bonded to a sapphire substrate. As the instantaneous field of view subtended at the photoconductor detector is exposed to the scene, free electrons are released according to the photons arriving. A potential is maintained across the length of the SPRITE, and this causes the electrons to drift toward the anode (see Figure 2.13). As the charge drifts under the potential field, the instantaneous field of view is scanned in the drift direction. The impact is to essentially create a TDI on the detector itself. On any array there are several bars, which avoids the need to scan each bar through every picture element every frame. A disadvantage of the SPRITE is that, as the charge drifts, it also spreads, which causes a loss in MTF. The SPRITE lends itself to a serial scan as distinct from the U.S. parallel scanned common module device. From considerations of noise one would expect a U.S. common module FLIR to outperform a SPRITE-based FLIR. Experience shows that the difference is not as marked as one would first anticipate, and the reason lies in not being able to extract

SPRITE

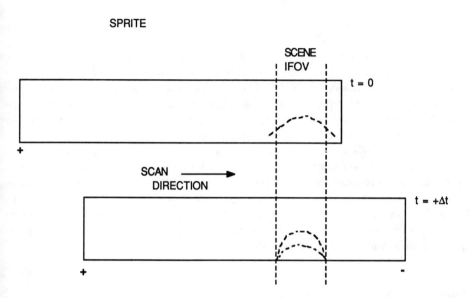

Figure 2.13 Operation of a SPRITE detector.

the maximum detectivity from each detector element in the U.S. array. Channels have to be balanced to get a uniform picture and this forces the U.S. common module sensitivity to correspond to the lowest sensitivity element in the column.

Up until the mid-1980s the majority of military FLIR designs revolved around the U.S. common module and the SPRITE detector. More recently the U.S. DOD and its British equivalent have pushed for future systems to be focal plane arrays, and potentially focal plane staring arrays. This has led to the development of what is known as second-generation and third-generation focal plane arrays. A second-generation focal plane array is a detector array with some processing integrated into the detector element that provides video out at the edge of the array without having individual wires to each element. The usual method of achieving this is a similar clocking mechanism described in the section on the CCD TV. Having none of the individual wiring as associated with the common module, focal plane arrays are less expensive to fabricate and much more reliable. Their performance is also proving to be significantly better. Focal plane arrays of MCT material now exceed 500 vertical elements. The thrust with the third-generation focal plane arrays is to develop uncooled arrays of capability similar to the cooled arrays. Although these are still limited to research, there are signs that this will be achieved both in the United States and the United Kingdom. Even if this is not a total success but can achieve equivalent performance at somewhat elevated temperatures from liquid nitrogen (i.e., 77 K) at a level whereby Peltier coolers can be used to provide the cryogenic source, a major limitation in modern FLIRs, that of cryogenic source reliability, will be defeated.

Two-dimensional arrays have been developed. These are full staring arrays requiring no scanning mechanism. Initially these two-dimensional arrays were of only limited size; that is, 16 × 16. They found immediate application in missile applications. The principal material was platinum silicide and the work was constrained therefore to the 3–5 μm band. PtSi arrays have grown recently such that 1024 × 1024 arrays have been demonstrated in laboratories.

As stated earlier, the majority of devices used in cameras covering the 3–5 and 8–14 μm bands are solid-state devices. No photoemissive materials are currently available having responsivity much beyond 1.2 μm. Photoconductive materials can be made having excitation energies corresponding to tenths and even hundredths of an electron volt. However, as already explained, such materials require cooling to prevent thermal excitation from obscuring the signal. In the 8–14 μm band the mercury cadmium telluride devices dominate.

2.4.4 Advances in Detectors and Applications

Detectors continue to advance but the advancement in the IR band is likely to be conservative due to the expense of developing a new detector-dewar arrangement. In the infrared band we are likely to see the HgCdTe devices dominate for at least the next five years. However, the form of the HgCdTe will evolve, whether it will be discrete detectors, column detectors, bar (SPRITE-like) detectors, or full focal plane arrays will be of interest to the sensor system engineer.

Recently we have seen a growth in the market for optical detectors covering the full range of the optical spectrum and reaching down to the soft x-ray region. Along with the increase in the products that have been well established in the market, new developments are stretching the limits of the emerging types and are finding new applications for others.

Silicon (Si) with its Schottky diode thin-film detectors and *focal plane arrays* (FPAs) leads the field. But indium antimonide (InSb) and mercury cadmium telluride are advancing strongly. The military continues to be a heavy investor in infrared IR detectors with greatest emphasis on MCT as a photoconductive and photovoltaic material. For far IR applications the military is also pursuing the development of mercury manganese telluride (HgMnTe) and mercury zinc telluride (HgZnTe). Very little research is being carried out in photoemissive and thermal devices, whereas considerable work is being undertaken in semiconductor materials such as silicon (Si), germanium (Ge), lead sulphide (PbS), lead selenide (PbSe), cadmium sulphide and cadmium selenide (CdS and CdSe), indium antimonide (InSb), HgCdTe, indium gallium arsenide (InGaAs), HgMnTe, and HgZnTe.

2.4.5   A Look into the Future

We have seen amazing advances in the field of infrared imagers. With the growth of thousands, maybe millions, of active elements on a chip, an even more promising future is held for the industry. The key will be affordability and reliability. The industry aim is a 1 cent per detector element in 1990 dollars. The industry still has a long way to go. The key to high-performance, cost-effective imaging sensors is (1) optical material selection and preparation, (2) development of high-yield fabrication processes, and (3) design of array architectures with the lowest possible complexity compatible with the functional requirements.

Sensor materials will continue to be addressed covering both extrinsic and intrinsic semiconductor monomers and compounds [1]. In the latter category more binary and ternary II–VI and III–V compounds will be investigated. The research in controlling the purity of MCT will continue, and large MCT focal plane arrays will be built, continuing the dominance of MCT in the infrared arena. Both hybrid and monolithic focal plane array developments will continue, with monolithic devices focusing in on intrinsic materials such as MCT, InSb, and silicon. Detection mechanisms will cover the range from photoconductors and photovoltaic junctions and Schottky diodes through to metal-insulator semiconductor–based charge storage sensor.

REFERENCE

1.   P.R. Norton, "Infrared Image Sensors," *Opt. Eng.*, Vol. 30, No. 11, November 1991, pp. 1649–1663.

Chapter 3
Sources and Transfer of Radiation

3.1 RADIOMETRIC AND PHOTOMETRIC QUANTITIES

A number of radiometric or photometric quantities will be useful to describe the origination and transfer of electromagnetic energy from the scene to the system. There is a one-to-one correspondence between radiometric and photometric quantities, with the latter simply being the former evaluated in terms of their effectiveness in stimulating the human eye. Therefore the photometric quantities always involve the luminous efficacy of the eye, $K(\lambda)$, which is the response of the eye normalized to 683 lumens per watt at the peak wavelength 555 nm. Table 3.1 summarizes these variables.

The subscript e is used for radiometric quantities and v for photometric quantities, whereas the unsubscripted symbol will be used to stand for the general quantity (radiometric or photometric). In the definitions of sterance, the symbol dA_n means an element of area normal to the viewing direction. It may also be noted here that 1 nit is the same as 1 candela/m² (cd/m²), which is also often seen in the literature. Both exitance and incidence have the same dimensions of flux per unit area, but the former is flux exiting an area and the latter is flux impinging on an area. In this regard the name *lux* is used only for illuminance, not luminous exitance.

Unfortunately there is a profusion of luminous units that are used by people in the field. Although we shall try to stick to the MKS units of Table 3.1, one other luminance unit is used so often that we cannot avoid mentioning it. The footlambert (fL) is defined as a luminance of π^{-1} candela/ft². We have the conversions 1 nit = .292 fL, 1 fL = 3.426 nits.

The spectral radiant quantities are functions of wavelength and defined as the corresponding radiant quantities per unit wavelength. Usually the unit of wavelength used is the micrometer (μm). These spectral quantities have the subscript

---

Table 3.1
Radiometric and Photometric Variables

Name	Symbol	Definition	Units
Flux	ϕ		
Radiant flux	ϕ_e		watts, W
Luminous flux	ϕ_v	$\int K(\lambda)\phi_\lambda d\lambda$	lumens, lm
Exitance	M	$\dfrac{d\phi}{dA}$	
Radiant exitance	M_e	$\dfrac{d\phi_e}{dA}$	W/m^2
Luminous exitance	M_v	$\dfrac{d\phi_v}{dA}$	lm/m^2
Intensity	I	$\dfrac{d\phi}{d\Omega}$	
Radiant intensity	I_e	$\dfrac{d\phi_e}{d\Omega}$	W/sr
Luminous intensity	I_v	$\dfrac{d\phi_v}{d\Omega}$	lm/sr (candela)
Sterance	L	$\dfrac{d^2\phi}{dA_n d\Omega} = \dfrac{dI}{dA_n}$	
Radiant sterance (radiance)	L_e	$\dfrac{dI_e}{dA_n}$	W/m^2/sr
Luminous sterance (luminance)	L_v	$\dfrac{dI_v}{dA_n}$	lm/m^2/sr (nit)
Incidance	E	$\dfrac{d\phi}{dA}$	
Radiant incidance (irradiance)	E_e	$\dfrac{d\phi_e}{dA}$	W/m^2
Luminous incidance (illuminance)	E_v	$\dfrac{d\phi_v}{dA}$	lm/m^2 (lux)

λ. Just such a spectral quantity is used in the definition of luminous flux in Table 3.1. The spectral radiant quantities are summarized in Table 3.2.

3.2 PHYSICAL LAWS OF RADIOMETRY

3.2.1 Planck's Law

The simplest radiator of energy to treat theoretically is one that absorbs all electromagnetic radiation of any wavelength falling on it. Such a body is known as a

Table 3.2
Spectral Radiometric Quantities

Name	Symbol	Definition	Units
Spectral radiant flux	ϕ_λ	$d\phi_e/d\lambda$	W/μm
Spectral radiant exitance	M_λ	$dM_e/d\lambda$	W/m^2/μm
Spectral radiant intensity	I_λ	$dI_e/d\lambda$	W/sr/μm
Spectral radiance	L_λ	$dL_e/d\lambda$	W/m^2/sr/μm
Spectral irradiance	E_λ	$dE_e/d\lambda$	W/m^2/μm

blackbody or a perfect radiator. The most fundamental law of electromagnetic radiation is Planck's law, which gives the spectral radiant exitance from a blackbody:

$$M_{BB\lambda} = \frac{C_1}{\lambda^5[\exp(C_2/\lambda T) - 1]} \tag{3.1}$$

where

$C_1 = 3.74 \times 10^8$ W μm^4/m^2
$C_2 = 1.44 \times 10^4$ μm K
T = absolute temperature in K.

3.2.2 Wien's Displacement Law

Figure 3.1 shows blackbody spectral radiant exitance as a function of wavelength with temperature as a parameter. Note that the wavelength at the peak of the curve, λ_m, shifts toward smaller values as the temperature increases. This behavior is expressed by Wien's displacement law:

$$\lambda_m T = 2898 \ \mu\text{m K} \tag{3.2}$$

3.2.3 Stefan-Boltzmann Law

The blackbody radiant exitance may be found by integrating (3.1) over all wavelengths, which leads to the Stefan-Boltzmann law:

$$M = \int_0^\infty M_{BB\lambda} \, d\lambda = \sigma T^4 \tag{3.3}$$

where $\sigma = 5.67 \times 10^{-8}$ W/m^2/K^4 (Stefan-Boltzmann constant).

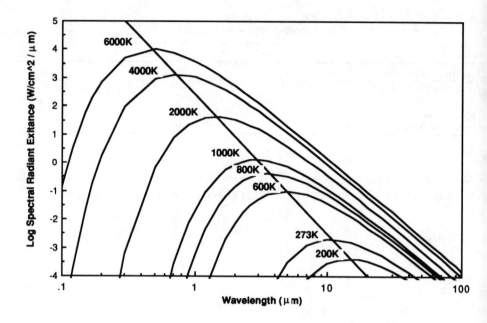

Figure 3.1 Blackbody spectral radiant exitance for different wavelengths.

3.2.4 Kirchhoff's Law

Real substances in general are not perfect radiators, and such cases are handled by introducing the spectral emissivity, ϵ_λ, and the total emissivity, ϵ, of the body in question. These are defined by

$$M_\lambda \equiv \epsilon_\lambda \cdot M_{BB\lambda} \tag{3.4}$$

$$M = \int_0^\infty M_\lambda \, d\lambda \equiv \epsilon \sigma T^4 \tag{3.5}$$

Both ϵ and ϵ_λ will be dimensionless quantities with values less than unity. Also both generally are functions of the nature of the radiating surface and can show some small dependence on temperature. For our purposes the temperature dependence can be ignored. Obviously $\epsilon = \epsilon_\lambda = 1$ for a blackbody.

For any surface, the fraction of incident spectral radiant flux at any wavelength that is absorbed is called the *spectral absorptivity*, α_λ, of the surface. Similarly the total absorptivity, α, is the fraction of the total radiant flux absorbed by a surface. Analogous quantities spectral reflectivity, ρ_λ, reflectivity, ρ, spectral transmissivity,

τ_λ, and transmissivity, τ, give the fractions reflected and transmitted, respectively, by the surface. Because absorption, reflection, and transmission represent all the possible fates for radiation impinging on a surface, we must have

$$\alpha_\lambda + \rho_\lambda + \tau_\lambda = 1 \qquad (3.6a)$$

$$\alpha + \rho + \tau = 1 \qquad (3.6b)$$

Absorptivity, reflectivity, and transmissivity are also known as *absorptance, reflectance,* and *transmittance,* respectively.

Kirchhoff's law says that absorptivity and emissivity for any surface must be equal:

$$\epsilon_\lambda = \alpha_\lambda \qquad (3.7a)$$

$$\epsilon = \alpha \qquad (3.7b)$$

For the surfaces and wavelengths we will be dealing with, we may also consider the transmissivity to be negligible. Thus, (3.6) and (3.7) lead to

$$\epsilon_\lambda = 1 - \rho_\lambda \qquad (3.8a)$$

$$\epsilon = 1 - \rho \qquad (3.8b)$$

3.2.5 Lambert's Law

It is approximately true for many surfaces (and exactly true for blackbodies) that their sterance is independent of viewing angle. Such surfaces are called *Lambertian surfaces* because they obey Lambert's law. Lambert's law may be derived by considering the intensity from a small surface, ΔA, as shown in Figure 3.2. The angle, θ, represents the viewing angle measured from the normal, so it is clear that $\Delta A_n = \Delta A \cdot \cos \theta$.

$$I(\theta) = L(\theta) \cdot \Delta A_n = L(\theta) \cdot \Delta A \cdot \cos \theta \qquad (3.9)$$

But as L is really independent of θ if we have a Lambertian surface then $L(\theta) = L(0)$ and

$$I(\theta) = L(0) \cdot \Delta A \cdot \cos \theta = I(0) \cos \theta \qquad (3.10)$$

which is Lambert's law, giving intensity as a function of viewing angle.

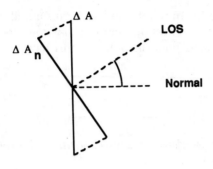

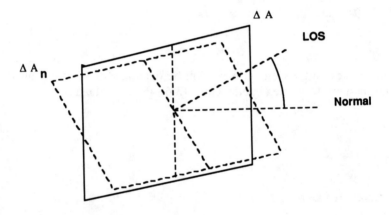

Figure 3.2 Projected area normal to the line of sight.

An additional result follows for Lambertian surfaces, relating exitance to sterance. Figure 3.3 shows an element, dA, of a surface radiating in accordance with Lambert's law. The infinitesimal flux radiated into the element of solid angle $d\Omega$ is, from the definition of sterance,

$$d^2\phi = L \cdot dA \cdot \cos\theta \cdot d\Omega$$

But the element of solid angle shown as the conical shell is just the area of the strip swept out on the sphere divided by R^2:

$$d\Omega = 2\pi R \cdot \sin\theta \cdot Rd\theta / R^2$$

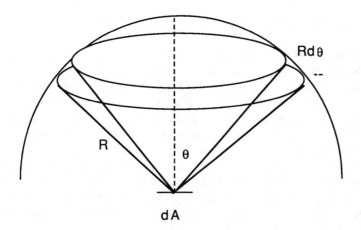

Figure 3.3 Flux from dA into the element of a solid angle (conical shell).

Therefore the total flux from dA into the hemisphere is

$$d_\phi = 2\pi L dA \int_0^{\pi/2} \cos\theta \cdot \sin\theta \cdot d\theta = \pi L dA$$

So radiant exitance,

$$M = d\phi/dA = \pi L \tag{3.11}$$

3.3 CALCULATION AIDS AND DATA SOURCES

The blackbody spectral radiant exitance curves of Figure 3.1 are designed to be in a very useful form, because on the scale used they are all the same shape. Therefore a transparent overlay of the curve shape could be made, and it could be adjusted to any temperature by moving its peak along the straight line, which just expresses Wien's displacement law, until it is over the desired temperature.

Even more useful is a device like the the GE radiation slide rule. Although these are no longer made, many are still in use. With a single temperature setting, various scales on the slide rule allow one to read off total radiant exitance, peak spectral radiant exitance, spectral radiant exitance at any wavelength, and integrated spectral radiant exitance from $\lambda = 0$ up to any wavelength. The back side of the device even has scales for radiant exitance in photons and for irradiance as function of range. A nearly identical slide rule is now available, as the IRIA infrared radiation calculator, from the Infrared Information Analysis Center (IRIA) of the

Environmental Research Institute of Michigan (ERIM). This calculator is pictured in Figure 3.4.

The Infrared Handbook prepared by the same center (IRIA) for the Office of Naval Research is the most authoritative source of nomenclature and symbology in the infrared field. In addition to the laws of radiometry it contains some data on spectral emissivities of materials, as well as information about infrared detectors and systems. The older, pre-1978, version of this source was entitled *Handbook of Military Infrared Technology* and contains a few useful emissivity curves omitted from the later version.

The largest collection of spectral emissivity data known to us is the massive *Data Compilation of Target and Background Characteristics*, prepared by the University of Michigan for the Air Force Avionics Laboratory. Much of the data is in the visible or near IR, but some is in the far IR. (Figure 4.1 shows the type of data available in this reference.)

Another very useful handbook is the *RCA Electro-Optics Handbook*. This has summaries of radiometric and photometric quantities, laws of radiometry, and a large amount of data on sources and transmission of visible radiation.

3.4   THE GEOMETRY OF RADIATIVE TRANSFER

In this section we explore the geometry of the transfer of radiation from one element of area, dA_1, to another, dA_2, as shown in Figure 3.5. The solid angle subtended by dA_2 at dA_1 is called $d\Omega_1$, while that subtended by 1 at 2 is called $d\Omega_2$. From our definitions, the flux from dA_1 received by dA_2 is given by

$$d^2\phi = dI(\theta_1) \cdot d\Omega_1 = dI(\theta_1) \cdot dA_2 \cos\theta_2 / R^2$$

The incidence of dA_2 from dA_1 is then

$$dE = d^2\phi/dA_2 = dI(\theta_1) \cdot \cos\theta_2 / R^2 \tag{3.12}$$

We may also write the intensity from dA_1 as

$$dI(\theta_1) = L(\theta_1) \cdot dA_1 \cos\theta_1 \tag{3.13}$$

Substituting (3.13) into (3.12) gives

$$dE = L(\theta_1) \cdot dA_1 \cos\theta_1 \cdot \cos\theta_2 / R^2 = L(\theta_1) \cdot \cos\theta_2 \cdot d\Omega_2 \tag{3.14}$$

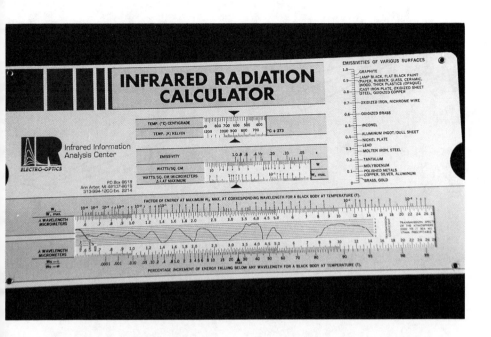

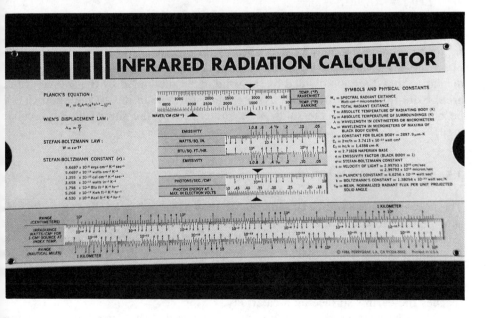

Figure 3.4 ERIM radiation calculator.

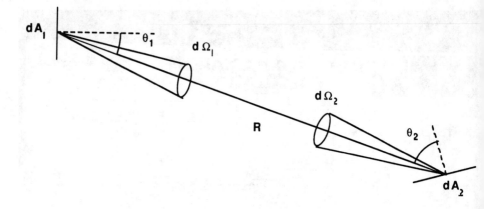

Figure 3.5 Geometry of radiative transfer from dA_1 to dA_2.

If we define dE_n as the incidence on the component of dA_2 normal to R then it is given by $dE/\cos\theta_2$, and we may change (3.14) to

$$L(\theta_1) = dE_n/d\Omega_2 \tag{3.15}$$

Equation (3.15) represents a very convenient starting point for many radiative transfer problems and may be described as the sterance from an elementary area of source in a given direction equals the incidence on an elementary area perpendicular to that direction divided by the solid angle subtended by the source at that area. Note that range drops out as an explicit variable in this formulation (it will be needed to calculate the solid angle subtended by the source at the receiver area).

3.5 SOURCES IN NATURE

The primary natural source of radiation in the visible and near-IR is of course the sun. Figure 3.6 shows the spectral irradiance from the sun out to 3.3 μm. Note that the spectral curve for the sun outside the earth's atmosphere is much like what one would expect from a 5900 K blackbody, whereas the curve at sea level shows the effect of absorption by molecules in the atmosphere. The total irradiance from the sun at the top of the atmosphere is about 1353 W m^{-2} and perhaps half of that reaches the earth's surface on a clear day.

The designation $m = 1$ in Figure 3.6 means that the sun's radiation is considered to be passing through just one thickness of the earth's atmosphere; this is called an *air mass of 1*. Therefore the sun must be directly overhead, for if it were off at any angle from the zenith, the path of its radiation through the atmosphere would be longer. For angles less than about 72°, the air mass (number of atmospheric thicknesses through which the radiation passes) is closely approximated by the secant of the source zenith angle:

$$m = \sec z \tag{3.16}$$

For larger angles (3.16) would require correction for atmospheric refraction.

Obviously for larger air masses (lower sun angles) less radiation reaches the earth's surface. This effect is illustrated by Figure 3.7. The figure also introduces the additional complication, at least in the visible region, that objects on the earth's surface are illuminated by sky light as well as direct sunlight: the global curves of Figure 3.7 are for combined sunlight plus sky light. It can be seen that sky light

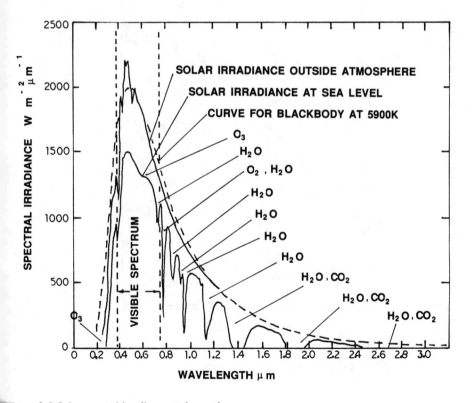

Figure 3.6 Solar spectral irradiance at the earth.

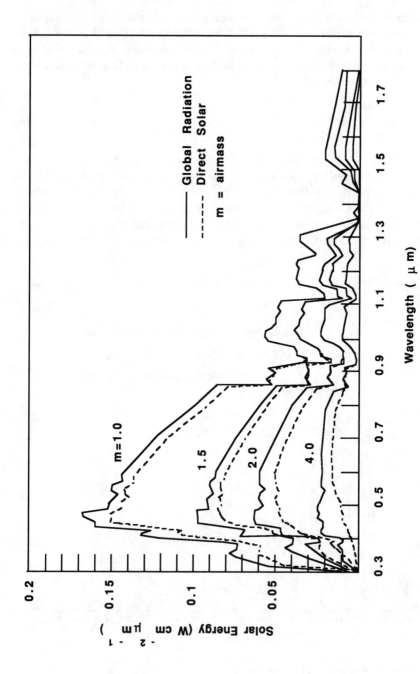

Figure 3.7 Solar spectral irradiance at the earth for different air masses. (Courtesy of David Gates, *Science*, Vol. 151, 1966, pp. 523–529.)

can be a significant fraction of the total, particularly at larger air masses. In fact, for objects in the shade, sky light is the *major* source of illumination, although there is some contribution due to light reflected from surroundings. Although sky light is just scattered sunlight, its spectral distribution is considerably different, peaking in the blue part of the visible spectrum and varying slightly with solar elevation. Figure 3.8 illustrates these characteristics. Only very ambitious models that try to capture subtle effects like color would be much concerned with these spectral changes.

Another factor that influences received radiation in the visible and near-IR is cloudiness. The effect of cloud conditions on spectral distribution is indicated by Figure 3.9, which shows that clouds (not surprisingly) tend to take the blue out of the received visible. The approximate effect on total received light can be seen from Table 3.3.

Table 3.3 takes us into the realm of the night sky, where sources of visible and near-IR radiation are the moon and stars. Again not only do we have different totals, as indicated by the table, but also subtle spectral changes. As in the daytime, spectral distributions are influenced not only by the presence of various sources, but also by cloud conditions, as illustrated by Figures 3.10 and 3.11.

These spectral characteristics of nighttime sources may be of interest if we are concerned with low light level TV systems or image intensifiers, but often FLIRs working in the 8–12 μm band are the system of choice at night. In this wavelength region the irradiance from sources like the stars and moon (and even the sun if it were up) is considered negligible compared to the thermal emission of the scene itself. One source that may not be negligible is the emission from the surrounding atmosphere. Figure 3.12 shows the spectral radiance of the night sky at several elevation angles. If the radiance were uniform across the sky, we would have for spectral irradiance on a horizontal surface:

$$E_\lambda = \pi L_\lambda \qquad (3.17)$$

Then for a Lambertian diffuse reflecting surface, spectral radiant exitance would be

$$M_\lambda = \rho_\lambda E_\lambda = \rho_\lambda \pi L_\lambda \qquad (3.18)$$

Now Figure 3.1 indicates that we can expect emitted values of M_λ on the order of only 1000–2000 μW cm^{-2} μm^{-1} for a 300 K blackbody. However the values in Figure 3.12 along with (3.18) indicate that reflected M_λ might be only a little less, depending on ρ_λ.

In Chapter 5, we shall be discussing available atmospheric computer models that will also perform atmospheric radiance calculations. The output from such models may be integrated over the hemisphere of the sky to L_λ values for use in calculated reflected M_λ.

60

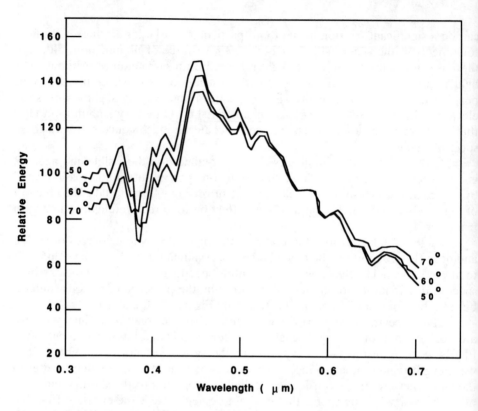

Figure 3.8 Spectral energy distribution of sky light for solar altitudes of 70°, 60°, and 50°. (Courtesy of H.R. Condit and F. Grum, "Spectral Energy Distribution of Daylight," *J. Opt. Soc. Am.*, Vol. 54, No. 7, 1964, pp. 937–944.)

Table 3.3
Surface Illuminance from Natural Sources

Sky Condition	Approximate Illuminance (lux)
Direct sunlight	10^5
Full daylight	10^4
Overcast day	10^3
Very dark day	10^2
Twilight	10
Deep twilight	1
Full moon	10^{-1}
Quarter moon	10^{-2}
Moonless, clear night	10^{-3}
Moonless, overcast night	10^{-4}

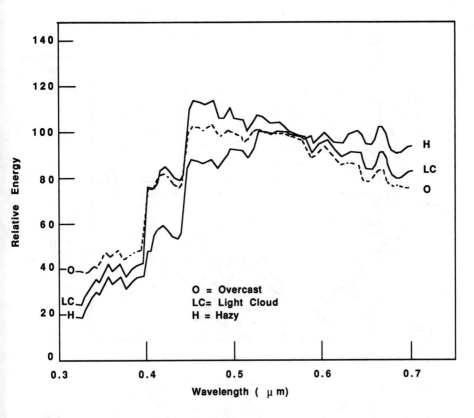

Figure 3.9 Spectral energy distribution of Daylight: hazy = *H*, clear = *C*, light clouds = *LC*, overcast = *O*. (Courtesy of H.R. Condit and F. Grum, "Spectral Energy Distribution of Daylight," *J. Opt. Soc. Am.*, Vol. 54, No. 7, 1964, pp. 937–944.)

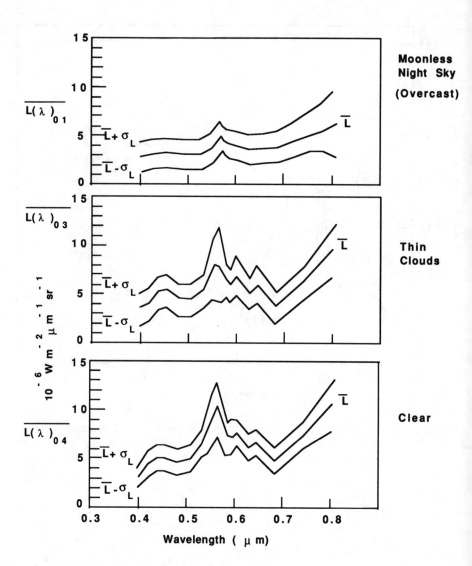

Figure 3.10 Mean spectral radiance and standard deviation for the moonless night sky. (Courtesy of D.H. Hohn and W. Büchtemann, "Spectral Radiance in the S20 Range and Luminance of the Clear and Overcast Night Sky," *Appl. Opt.*, Vol. 12, No. 1, 1973, pp. 52–61.)

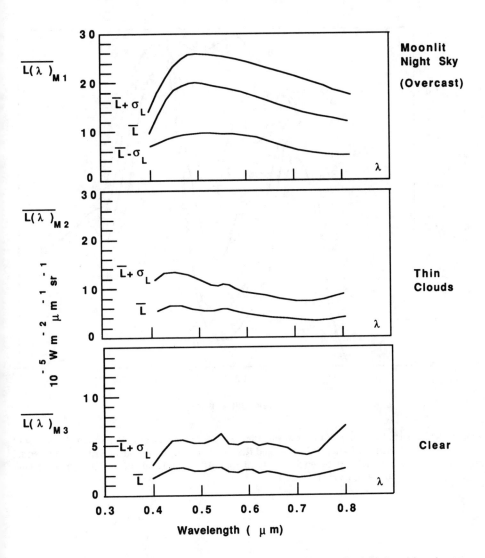

Figure 3.11 Mean spectral radiance and standard deviation for the moonlit night sky with various types of sky cover. (Courtesy of D.H. Hohn and W. Büchtemann, "Spectral Radiance in the S20 Range and Luminance of the Clear and Overcast Night Sky," *Appl. Opt.*, Vol. 12, No. 1, 1973, pp. 52–61.)

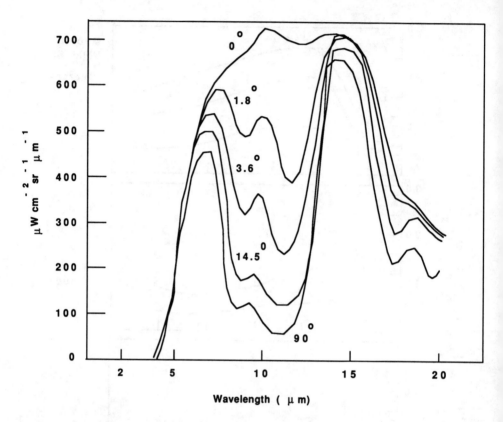

Figure 3.12 Spectral radiance of the clear nighttime sky for several angles of elevation. (Courtesy of E.E. Bell, L. Eisner, J. Young, and R.A. Oetjen, "Spectral Radiance of Sky and Terrain at Wavelengths Between 1 and 20 Microns. II. Sky Measurements," *J. Opt. Soc. Am.*, Vol. 50, 1960, pp. 1313–1320.)

Chapter 4
Targets and Backgrounds

4.1 BLACKBODIES, GRAYBODIES, AND REALITY

One of the most common approximations used in characterizing targets and backgrounds, both in the IR and visible regions of the spectrum, is to treat the spectral emissivities, absorptivities, and reflectivities of equations (3.7) and (3.8) as constants over the wavelength bands of interest. In fact, in the IR band the assumption is often made that the sources of radiation are blackbodies: $\epsilon = \epsilon_\lambda = 1$. Under this assumption, the shape of the curve of spectral radiance *versus* wavelength will be just that of Planck's law. From equations (3.1) and (3.11) it follows then that

$$L_\lambda = \frac{C_1}{\pi \lambda^5 [\exp(C_2/\lambda T) - 1]} \tag{4.1}$$

Of course, such an oversimplification cannot be made in the visible range because there we are using reflected radiation and the corresponding result would be for everything in the scene to be perfectly black. We would have no contrast and, correspondingly, no signal with which to acquire targets.

The next level in sophistication of scene spectral description would be to make ϵ independent of wavelength but less than unity: $\epsilon = \epsilon_\lambda = 1 - \rho_\lambda = 1 - \rho < 1$. Just as the previous case could be described as all blackbodies, this case would be all graybodies. In the visible region, this approximation would make all objects various shades of gray. In the IR region, the emitted spectral radiance is altered from the previous case, but the shape of the spectral curve is not changed:

$$L_\lambda = \frac{\epsilon C_1}{\pi \lambda^5 [\exp(C_2/\lambda T) - 1]} \tag{4.2}$$

Now there would also be a reflected spectral radiance in either the IR or visible, given, for Lambertian surfaces, by

$$L_{r\lambda} = \rho E_{s\lambda}/\pi \tag{4.3}$$

where $E_{s\lambda}$ is the scene spectral irradiance. Few models, in either the visible or IR range, surpass this level of sophistication in scene spectral description. The argument is often made that the visible band of wavelengths is small enough so that reflectivity variations across it are negligible, whereas objects in the far infrared region are really close to blackbodies. Yet such approximations must inevitably miss subtle interactions of scene radiance with spectral transmittance of the atmosphere and spectral response of the sensor. A model at this level is truly drab and colorless! We shall see shortly how valid the justification for this approximation really is.

A full spectral treatment of targets and backgrounds would recognize the fact that ϵ_λ (and ρ_λ) are functions of wavelength. Our previous equations for radiance are then modified to

$$L_\lambda = \frac{\epsilon_\lambda C_1}{\pi \lambda^5 [\exp(C_2/\lambda T) - 1]} \tag{4.4}$$

$$L_{r\lambda} = \rho_\lambda E_{s\lambda}/\pi \tag{4.5}$$

These equations are useful only insofar as we can find data specifying ϵ_λ or ρ_λ for common background and target materials.

4.1.1 Targets

Chapter 3 mentions several sources of data on targets and backgrounds. U.S. military targets are commonly painted an olive-drab. Figure 4.1 shows spectral reflectivity for just such a paint. One can easily see it is not a blackbody in either the mid IR (3–5 μm) or the far IR (8–12 μm) region, with $\epsilon \approx .9$ in the former and .8 in the latter, although it is a fair graybody in both regions. In the visible region, it is not even a very good graybody (indeed, it would not be called olive-drab if it were). Figure 4.2 shows spectral reflectivity curves for two olive-drab military uniform materials. It would be a very good approximation to call these two blackbodies in the 8–12 μm band, but they are not close to being graybodies in the 3–5 μm band, because of the variation in reflectivity they show in that spectral region.

For operation in snow, military targets are often painted white. Figure 4.3 shows spectral curves for a white paint on metal. In this case we have a very poor

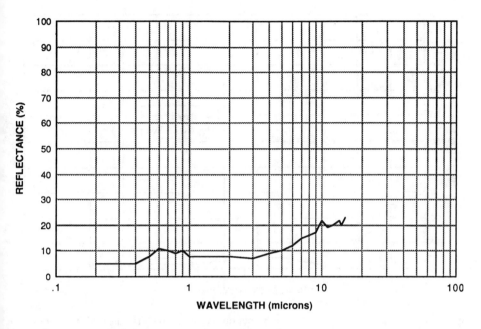

Figure 4.1 Spectral reflectivity of olive-drab paint: two coats on one coat of zinc chromate on resin impregnated fiberglass. (Data from *Data Compilation of Target and Background Characteristics*, University of Michigan for USAF Avionics Lab, 1967.)

approximation to even a graybody in the 3–5 μm band, and only a fair approximation to one in the 8–12 μm band. In neither band could such an object be reasonably called a *blackbody*.

Another possible target material for EO systems could be bare human skin, either because we are trying to detect humans against some background or because, for medical purposes, we wish to detect temperature variations on the exterior of the body. Here, at last we find a very good blackbody throughout the infrared [1]. Furthermore there appears to be no measurable difference between white and black skin at these wavelengths: in the infrared we are all black.

4.1.2 Backgrounds

4.1.2.1 Terrain Backgrounds

A general graph of spectral reflectances for many possible backgrounds is shown in Figure 4.4. The one curve for vegetation is of special interest because all green

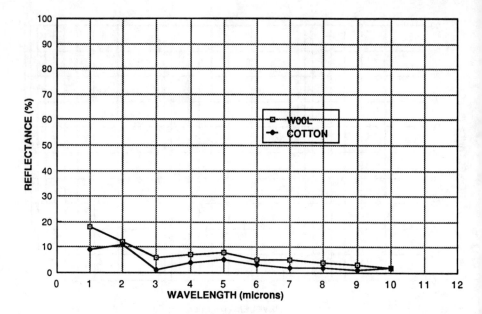

Figure 4.2 Spectral reflectivity of olive-drab uniform material: wool elastique OD #51 and cotton herringbone uniform fabric OD #7. (Data from *Handbook of Military Infrared Technology*, Office of Naval Research, 1965.)

plants approximate this curve fairly closely, with the large peak in the near IR and a smaller one in the 4–6 μm region. Note that in the 8–12 μm band, a graybody approximation with $\rho \approx$ 7–10% is not too bad. The curve of Figure 4.4 is very good for the leaves of deciduous trees, but the needles of conifers show an even flatter curve (see Figure 4.5) in the far IR range, being excellent blackbodies in that region.

In many battlefield situations, the vegetation in the immediate area may be stripped away so that targets are viewed against bare soil, or vegetation may have been absent in the first place in the desert. The curve for loam in Figure 4.4 gives some idea of what such a background may look like. For this background there does not appear to be any commonly used wavelength band, visible, near-IR, mid-IR, or far-IR, in which it is reasonable to make the blackbody or graybody assumption. Only in the 6–8 μm wavelength region is loam a blackbody, but that region is seldom used for systems because of strong absorption by H_2O in any atmospheric path.

Another important background could be snow, also represented by one curve of Figure 4.4 in the visible and near-IR regions. If we can assume that snow has optical properties like ice, we may use the curves of Figure 4.6 for the mid- and

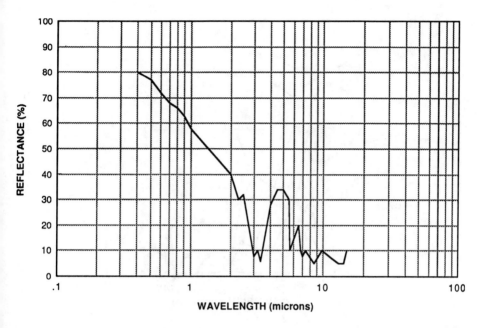

Figure 4.3 Spectral reflectivity of white paint: flat white acrylic resin on 22 mil stainless steel. (Data from *Data Compilation of Target and Background Characteristics*, University of Michigan for USAF Avionics Lab, 1967.)

far-IR regions. The curves indicate that ice is very "dark" in those bands, but shows its greatest spectral variation just there.

4.1.2.2 Marine Backgrounds

In some respects, water has a spectral reflectance curve shaped similar to that of ice, with a dip in the 3–5 μm band and another just beyond 10 μm. Furthermore, there is no practical difference between seawater and pure water in this regard [2]. However, whereas ice in the form of snow may be thought of as a diffuse reflector, the surface of a body of water is definitely specular. This fact introduces two more variables in the description of the optical and IR properties of a marine background: direction and sea surface state (due to wind).

Figure 4.7 illustrates the effect of the first of these, showing spectral reflectivity with viewing angle (measured from the surface normal) as a parameter. We can see that a flat water surface should be a pretty good blackbody at all wavelengths out to 10 μm when viewed normally, but when viewed along the surface it is a pretty good mirror (50–70% reflectance).

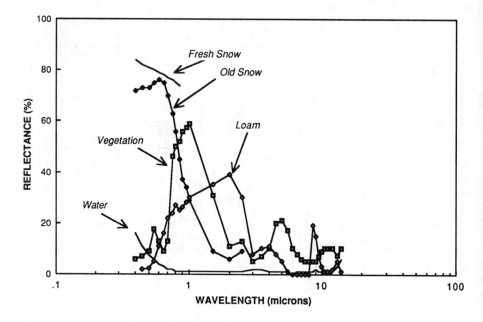

Figure 4.4 Spectral reflectivity of various backgrounds.

Both the reflected and emitted radiation are affected in general by a roughened sea surface, or waves. Figures 4.8 and 4.9 show how reflected solar and sky radiance are affected. Not surprisingly, waves alter the reflectance much more significantly for grazing angles than for near normal. Emitted spectral radiance is also affected, as shown by Figure 4.10.

4.1.2.3 Sky Backgrounds

The radiation from the sky under various conditions has already been considered in Section 3.5, in the sense of a source that irradiates targets and backgrounds. Here we regard it in the sense of an actual background for targets that are higher in altitude than the sensor. The curves of Figures 3.6 through 3.11 may be consulted to characterize many sky backgrounds that might arise in some scenario. Probably the best way to model a sky background in the visible or IR region is to use one of the atmospheric models discussed in Chapter 5, LOWTRAN or UVTRAN if available, in the radiance mode to produce the sky radiance at the specific look angles of interest.

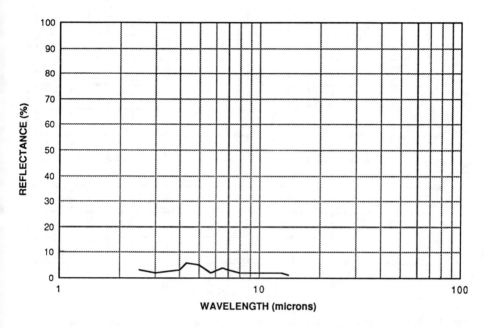

Figure 4.5 Spectral reflectivity of Ponderosa pine needles. (Data from *Data Compilation of Target and Background Characteristics*, University of Michigan for USAF Avionics Lab, 1967.)

4.2 UNIFORM AND NONUNIFORM SCENES

Aside from the flat spectral assumption, one other commonly used simplifying assumption is that of uniform targets and backgrounds. That is, both target and background are assumed to be the same everywhere, spatially. Obviously, this assumption is not true, but it was forced on modelers for two reasons. First, the early computers on which models were run were too limited in memory or too slow (or both) to handle detailed descriptions of targets or backgrounds. The rapid advance of computer technology has made this reason invalid. The second reason, and the one that still represents a major stumbling block, is that, even if a minutely detailed scene description were built into the model, ultimately we do not know what to do with it. The models we are concerned with generally end with some human acquisition probability, and we lack the psychophysical data to predict the effect of small scene details on this probability. Almost all psychophysical acquisition experiments have been done with very simple targets and backgrounds (simple uniform target shapes against uniform backgrounds or bar patterns, and so on).

Even if we wished to perform experiments to relate human acquisition to scene details, we would be at a loss as to what nonuniform targets and backgrounds

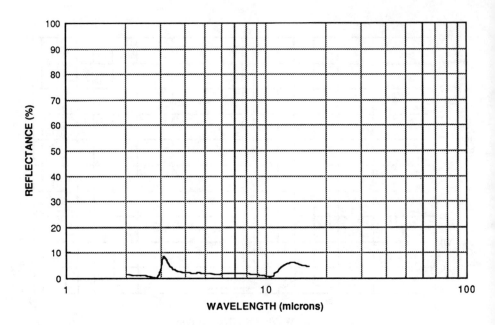

Figure 4.6 Spectral reflectivity of ice. (Data from Schaaf and Williams, "Optical Constants of Ice in Infrared," *J. Opt. Soc. Am*, Vol. 63, No. 6, 1973, pp. 726–732.)

to use: the possibilities in all their permutations and combinations are enormous. One possible way out of the quandary is to use a statistical approach and classify scenes according to a few metrics that discriminate between scenes according to their tractability to acquisition in general. Then only the scene metrics, rather than some detailed description, would be required as input to the model: scenes would be treated by class rather than individually. This approach is one that we feel is very promising and yet very little explored by the modeling community so far.

4.2.1 Faceted Targets

There now exist IR target models that characterize the targets as a set of facets, each with its own temperature, size, emissivity, and orientation in three-dimensional space. One of the most remarkable of these is named *PRISM* (physically reasonable infrared signature model), developed by the U.S. Army Tank and Automotive Command (TACOM) at Keweenaw Research Center of Michigan Technological University in Houghton, Michigan. In addition to detailed input on the target, the user can enter meteorological data and terrain data, to receive output consisting of time histories of the target and terrain facet temperatures.

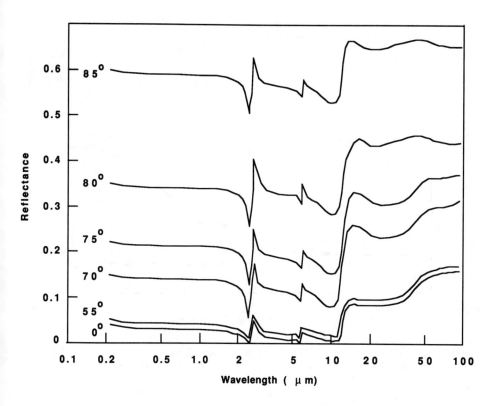

Figure 4.7 Spectral reflectivity of water (specular) viewing angle as parameter. (Courtesy of M. Sidran, "Broadband Reflectance and Emissivity of Specular and Rough Water Surfaces," *Appl. Opt.*, Vol. 20, No. 18, 1981, pp. 3176–3183.)

As noted previously, such detailed scene data can be too much for any subsequent acquisition model that accepts it as input. Therefore PRISM can also produce area-weighted, radiometric temperature averages for the whole target as seen from any aspect angle, as well as hot spot determinations, either of which is a more appropriate input to present-day human acquisition models. In this regard we might add that it is somewhat disheartening to see such a magnificent model as PRISM enter into such a mismatch, rather like Prince Charming marrying one of the fat stepsisters because Cinderella never showed up at the ball.

More recently, a similar faceted model for aircraft has become available. This is PCNirATAM from the same company that produces PCTRAN (to be discussed in Chapter 5), a PC version of NIRATAM, a NATO computer model.

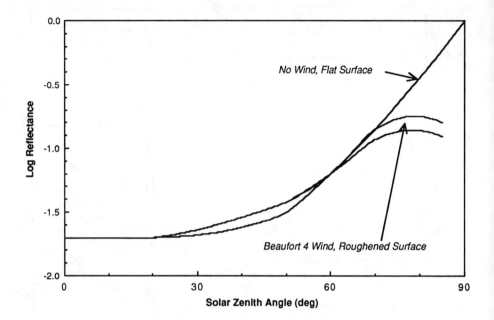

Figure 4.8 Total reflection of solar radiation from sea surface: the upper and lower curves from a wind-roughened surface show a possible range of values. (Data from *The Infrared Handbook*, Office of Naval Research, 1978.)

4.2.2 Background Statistics

Real terrain backgrounds in general are uniform neither in the visible nor the IR part of the spectrum. Although such backgrounds are quite random, something about their statistics is known. This means that at least something about the probability of given variations in the background can be calculated.

In the visible part of the spectrum there is evidence [3] that the distribution of luminances in a natural terrain scene is log normal. Expected average normalized luminance is .02; that is, if we multiply the illuminance on the surface by .02 we should get close to the average luminance from natural terrain. This value takes into account reflectance variations as well as surface orientations, texture and shading, and spatial variations in natural sources. The variance on $\ln(L)$ is expected to be 18 and the standard deviation of $\ln(L)$ is 4.24. Figure 4.11 shows this expected probability density function.

A number of statistical studies have been done in the 8–12 μm band. Most of these conclude (or assume) that natural terrain temperature distributions are

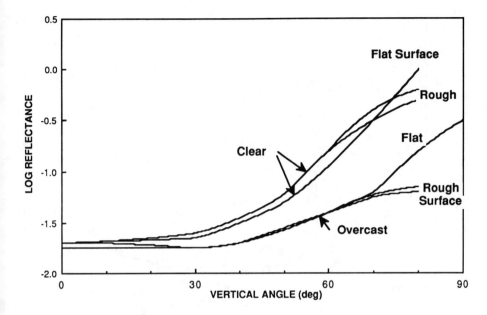

Figure 4.9 Log of sky radiance reflectance from sea surface. (Data from *The Infrared Handbook*, Office of Naval Research, 1978.)

Gaussian but spatially correlated [4, 5]. The scene temperature autocorrelation function can be approximated by a negative exponential:

$$\phi(r) = \sigma^2 \exp(-\alpha r) \tag{4.6}$$

where

r = separation of two measurement points
σ = scene temperature standard deviation
α = reciprocal of scene temperature correlation length.

Such a spatial correlation of temperature is to be expected. It is only common sense to suppose that if the temperature at one point on the terrain has a certain value, then nearby points are likely to have a similar value, and the closer the points are the more alike they will be. Experimental values for σ are in the range 1–7 K and for α^{-1} in the range 30–600 m. Actually a more careful analysis [6] indicates that the terrain temperature statistics shift slightly during the day, depend-

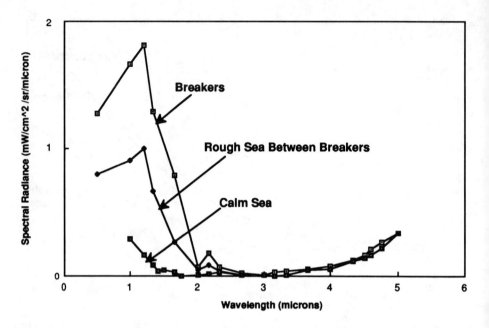

Figure 4.10 Spectral radiance of the ocean. (Data from *The Infrared Handbook*, Office of Naval Research, 1978.)

ing on the heat input variation to the surface, but this effect is below the resolution of most practical modeling efforts.

Surprisingly, the same sort of temperature statistics seem to apply to the sea surface: normal distribution of temperature with positive spatial correlation monotonically decreasing with distance [7]. In this case, because of waves, the standard deviation is highly dependent on wind speed and sensor depression angle. Figure 4.12 illustrates this dependence. From this figure we can also see that a larger depression angle (looking more straight downward) greatly reduces the temperature standard deviation seen, probably because it reduces the effect of the waves. In any case it can be seen that somewhat lower values of temperature standard deviation are to be expected from the sea surface than from terrain. The correlation length is less certain, but is said to be small compared to seaborne targets of interest (e.g., a frigate). Again this would be smaller than the value typical of terrain.

4.3 CLUTTER

Just knowing the statistics of the background helps little when it comes to modeling human acquisition of targets against that background. In fact any knowledge of

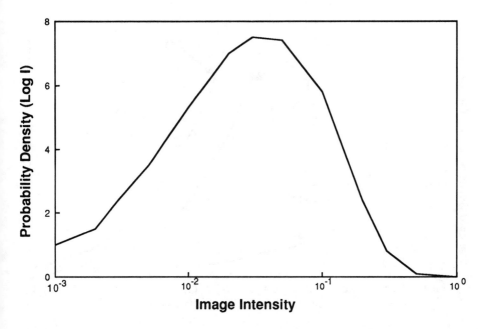

Figure 4.11 Probability density for luminance in a natural scene. (Data from [3].)

the background alone will be insufficient to predict its effects on acquisition: it is the characteristics of the background compared to those of the target that are important. One group of authors [8] has stated the case thus: "The most important aspect of complexity in target recognition probably has to do with the similarity of the target to the characteristics of the background." And in fact, experimental evidence [9] exists to confirm this viewpoint.

In this spirit, a normalized clutter measure has been defined [10] as the amount of background texture that is similar to the target in size, shape, and orientation. This measure has been related to human acquisition, through the experimental evidence mentioned previously. The definition is such that the clutter is an inherent property of the scene (target and background together), and independent of the sensor. In this respect, it is similar to the measure of inherent contrast. Furthermore it is symmetric with respect to target size and background texture size; it is always largest when the two are equal, but if either is twice the other, the clutter is reduced by the same amount. A uniform background always produces zero clutter by this measure, regardless of the target characteristics, and a background densely packed with texture elements that are all the same size, shape, and orientation as the target produces the maximum clutter of unity. The reader is referred to the original literature for details on clutter calculation, but it might be added here that a clutter

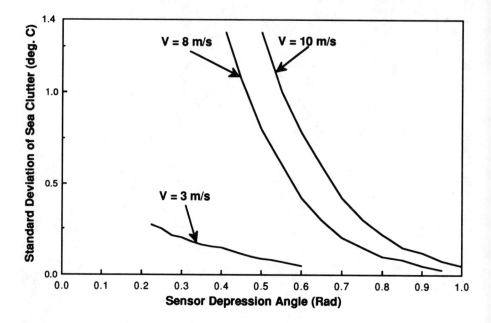

Figure 4.12 Standard deviation of sea clutter as a function of solar depression angle. (Data from [7].)

value of .25 or greater is large for most natural scenes and, unless the contrast is large, represents a formidable acquisition problem for human observers. Exactly how the clutter measure affects human acquisition is discussed in Chapter 7.

For targets at close range, or viewed with a sensor of high magnification, so that internal details are quite noticeable, it is probably better to define clutter in terms of the similarity between background texture and target texture. This approach also represents a novel way to quantify camouflage. However, although it is possible to form such definitions, the experimental evidence for connecting such a measure to human acquisition is lacking.

REFERENCES

1. D. Mitchell, C.H. Wyndham, and T. Hodgson, "Emissivity and Transmittance of Excised Human Skin in Its Thermal Emission Wave Band," *J. Appl. Psychology*, Vol. 23, No. 3, September 3, 1967, p. 390.

2. L.W. Pinkley and D. Williams, "Optical Properties of Sea Water in the Infrared," *J. Opt. Soc. Am.*, Vol. 66, No. 6, June 1976, p. 554.

3. W.A. Richards, "Lightness Scale from Image Intensity Distributions," *Appl. Opt.*, Vol. 21, No. 14, July 15, 1982, p. 2569.

4. N. Ben-Yosef, B. Rahat, and G. Feigin, "Simulation of IR Images of Natural Backgrounds," *Appl. Opt.*, Vol. 22, No. 1, January 1, 1983, p. 190.

5. N. Ben-Yosef, K. Wilner, S. Simhony, and G. Feigin, "Measurement and Analysis of 2-D Infrared Natural Background," *Appl. Opt.*, Vol. 24, No. 14, July 15, 1985, p. 2109.

6. N. Ben-Yosef *et al.*, "Natural Terrain Infrared Radiance Statistics: Daily Variation," *Appl. Opt.*, Vol. 24, No. 23, December 1, 1985, p. 4167.

7. I. Wilf and Y. Manor, "Simulation of Sea Surface Images in the Infrared," *Appl. Opt.*, Vol. 23, No. 18, September 15, 1984, p. 3174.

8. J.E. Nygaard *et al.*, "The Measurement of Stimulus Complexity in High-Resolution Sensor Imagery," Tech. Rep. AMRL-TDR-64-29, Aerospace Medical Research Laboratories, Wright-Patterson AFB, May 1964.

9. J.R. Bloomfield, "Visual Search in Complex Fields: Size Differences Between Target Disc and Surrounding Discs," *Human Factors*, Vol. 14, 1972, p. 139.

10. G. Waldman, J. Wootton, G. Hobson, and K. Luetkemeyer, "A Normalized Clutter Measure for Images," *Comp. Vis., Graphics, and Image Proc.*, Vol. 42, 1988, p. 137.

Chapter 5
Atmospherics

5.1 BASIC PROCESSES

There are four basic processes by which the atmosphere can affect electromagnetic radiation on its passage from the scene to the system:

1. *Absorption*: Atmospheric gases in the path may absorb some of the radiation.
2. *Scattering*: Atmospheric gases and suspended particles may scatter some radiation from the target out of the line of sight and some background radiation into the line of sight.
3. *Emission*: Atmospheric gases and suspended particles in the path may themselves radiate in the spectral band of interest.
4. *Turbulence*: Time-varying inhomogeneities in the refractive index of the atmosphere can blur the target image.

5.1.1 Extinction

The first two of these processes, absorption and scattering, are often grouped together under the heading of extinction or attenuation. To understand their effect we must reconsider the derivation of (3.15) from Chapter 3, because that treatment assumed a completely transparent medium between the emitting area and the receiving area. Consider the flux traveling through an infinitesimal thickness, dR, of a scattering and absorbing medium, as in Figure 5.1. Because of the removal of power by the two processes it is assumed that the change in flux, $d\phi$, is negative and proportional to both the entering flux and the thickness:

$$d\phi = -\beta_s \phi \cdot dR - \beta_a \phi \cdot dR \tag{5.1}$$

The first term in (5.1) is the flux lost from the beam due to scattering and the

---

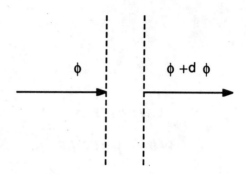

Figure 5.1 Change in flux through a medium.

second is that due to absorption. The term β_s is called the *scattering coefficient*, and β_a is called the *absorption coefficient*. It is not difficult to show that each of these is proportional to the density of attenuating particles of that type. They may be grouped together to give the extinction (or attenuation) coefficient, β:

$$\beta = \beta_s + \beta_a \tag{5.2}$$

So (5.1) becomes

$$d\phi = -\beta\phi \cdot dR \tag{5.3}$$

This may be integrated to give the result for a finite distance through an attenuating medium:

$$\phi = \phi_0 e^{-\beta R} \tag{5.4}$$

or

$$\phi = \tau\phi_0 \tag{5.5}$$

where $\tau = e^{-\beta R}$ is the transmissivity of the atmosphere at range R, as defined in Chapter 3.

It should be noted in all of these equations that the scattering, absorption, and extinction coefficients are usually strong functions of wavelength, so (5.4) and (5.5) are rigorously true only for spectral radiant flux. They would have to be integrated over a wavelength to be correct for a broad spectral band.

Returning to the derivation of (3.15), we can now see that the very first equation should have a factor of τ on the right for an attenuating medium. This change leads to a final result of

$$\tau L(\theta_1) = dE_n/d\Omega_2 \tag{5.6}$$

For a Lambertian source L is not a function of angle, so for a finite source subtending a small solid angle, Ω, at the receiver

$$E = \tau L \Omega = \tau(R) L A_s/R^2 \tag{5.7}$$

where A_s is the source area.

Equation (5.7) will be a sufficiently accurate method of finding incidance due to a single source at the entrance pupil to the imaging system in our applications, because we are usually dealing with narrow field-of-view systems so that even if the source is the whole background seen by the system, it still subtends a small solid angle and the radiation from all points is still arriving nearly along the optical axis. As mentioned earlier, the wavelength dependence of τ means that (5.7) is strictly true only for spectral irradiance.

Another way of looking at (5.7) is to define an apparent sterance at range R as

$$L(R) \equiv \tau(R)L \tag{5.8}$$

That is, the source appears the same as if it had a sterance $L(R)$ but was viewed through a perfectly clear medium. However, even (5.8) gives just the effective sterance directly from the one source considered; there will also be some sterance from other sources scattered by the atmosphere into the line of sight, and this can be important as we shall shortly see. Therefore it is more accurate to define the sterance at range R by

$$L(R) \equiv \tau(R)L + L_{is} \tag{5.9}$$

where L_{is} is the in-scattered sterance along the path. Then (5.7) becomes

$$E = L(R)A_s/R^2 \tag{5.10}$$

5.1.1.1 Scattering

In the process of scattering, a particle continuously extracts power from a passing electromagnetic wave and reradiates that power in all directions. The fraction of the wave's power extracted and the angular pattern of the reradiation is a function of the ratio of the size of the particle to the size of the wavelength. Because there may be a range of wavelengths in the spectral band of the system and there is a tremendous range of sizes of possible scattering particles, from individual gas molecules to raindrops, there are a great many possibilities to consider. Table 5.1 shows the range of sizes and concentrations of possible scattering particles.

Generally scattering is broken down into three wavelength regimes for ease of treatment. The first is where the wavelength is much larger than the size of the scattering particles. This situation is called *Rayleigh scattering*, and an approximate treatment shows that the scattering coefficient in this case is proportional to $1/\lambda^4$. Such a situation would apply to the case of scattering by individual, atmospheric gas molecules for visible or longer wavelengths. Rayleigh scattering gives rise to the blue color of the sky because of the $1/\lambda^4$ dependence. The angular distribution of the scattered radiation is symmetric about the scattering particle, showing equal forward and backward scattering.

The second wavelength regime occurs where the wavelength is comparable in size to the scattering particle and is the most difficult to calculate. This type is called *Mie scattering*. In this case the intensity of the scattered radiation becomes less dependent on wavelength and more dependent on angle, with a distinct peak in the forward direction. The theoretical expression developed for this case is an infinite series, the first term of which represents just Rayleigh scattering. Therefore Mie scattering is really the general case, and the result could be used for all wavelengths.

Finally, we have the case where the scattering particles are much larger than a wavelength, as for example raindrops scattering visible or IR radiation. This regime is called *nonselective scattering* or the *geometrical optics regime*. The first name stems from the fact that, as the scatterers becomes much larger than the wavelength, any dependence of scattered intensity on wavelength fades away: sometimes this is called *white light scattering* because all wavelengths are scattered equally. The results may be calculated approximately by using just geometrical optics. For nonselective scattering there is still a strong angular dependence in the scattered intensity and a strong peak in the forward direction. Figure 5.2 illustrates the angular patterns.

Table 5.1
Atmospheric Scattering Particles

Type	Radius (μm)	Density (cm⁻³)
Air molecules	10^{-4}	10^{19}
Haze particles	10^{-2}–1	10–10^3
Fog droplets	1–10	10–100
Raindrops	10^2–10^4	10^{-5}–10^{-2}

SMALL PARTICLES

Particles smaller than 1/10 wavelength

Pattern is symmetrical

Incident beam

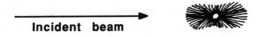

LARGE PARTICLES

Particles approximately 1/4 wavelength
Scattering concentrated in forward direction

Incident beam

LARGER PARTICLES

Particles larger than wavelength
Extreme concentration of forward scattering

Incident beam

Figure 5.2 Angular patterns of scattering.

5.1.1.2 Absorption

Absorption is basically a quantum process in which a quantum of electromagnetic energy (a photon) is absorbed by an atmospheric molecule, causing a change in the molecule's internal energy state. Conceivably an electron in one of the molecular atoms could change states by absorbing a photon, but in the normal atmospheric gases the electrons are so tightly bound to the atoms that it would take an ultraviolet or shorter wavelength photon to cause such a jump. Therefore we may ignore that possibility for our purposes. Instead we look at the absorption of a photon by a molecule that itself has a dipole moment. Such molecules have vibrational and rotational energy states, meaning they can absorb a photon and go into vibration or rotation, but the masses involved are so much larger than the electron's that the frequencies involved are much lower: a visible light photon has too much energy to cause the transition, but an IR photon might be just right. For this reason atmospheric absorption is usually not considered a problem in the visible region of the spectrum, but it definitely must be considered in the IR region.

As far as working in the IR range, we are fortunate that the two major constituents of the atmosphere, oxygen and nitrogen, are in the form of homonuclear, diatomic molecules, N_2 and O_2, so that they possess no electric dipole moment: because of symmetry there is no reason for electrons to spend more time at one end of the molecule than the other. With no dipole moment, the molecules will not absorb electromagnetic radiation. However, the next two atmospheric constituents of carbon dioxide, CO_2, and water, H_2O, are definite culprits in the absorption of infrared radiation. Figure 5.3 shows the absorption of the atmosphere *versus* wavelength in general, and the contributions from CO_2 and H_2O. If all or part of the optical path is at high altitude we would also have to be concerned with ozone, O_3 which has a large absorption band between 9 and 10 μm.

5.1.2 Emission

Like absorption, emission is a process we need worry about only for the IR region and not the visible one. Because the atmospheric gases are at some temperature above absolute 0, they will be emitting thermal radiation. We are often dealing with IR imaging systems that detect differences in radiance only between the target and the background. For these type systems, emitted radiation along the line of sight (called *path radiance*) will not be of importance if the path to the target is essentially the same as the path to the background. However, one important tactical situation in which the paths are not equivalent is the case of looking upward toward some airborne target; in this case the background is really just the path radiance of a path through the total atmosphere.

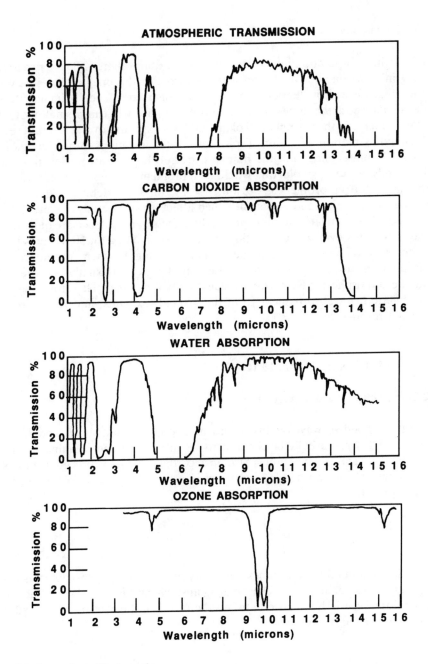

Figure 5.3 Atmospheric IR absorption.

5.1.3 Turbulence

Time-varying temperature inhomogeneities in the atmosphere will give rise to time-varying inhomogeneities in the refractive index. For the imaging systems we are considering, the major degradation caused by such turbulence is image blurring: the changing refractive index in the atmospheric path will cause small motions of the target image in the system focal plane, and any exposure over a few milliseconds will show this motion as a blur. Typical electronic imaging systems have a frame time of 33 milliseconds, and the human eye itself has an integration time of 100 milliseconds or more, so blurring would be a problem in either case. However, the turbulence blurring problem is obviously worse for small details in the image, as opposed to extinction and emission, which affect all size details equally.

As will be seen later in this chapter, the effects of turbulence are quite difficult to calculate. However, the calculation can often be avoided for IR systems because we are usually considering their performance at night, when turbulence in the atmosphere is at a minimum. During the day the ground usually becomes hotter than the atmosphere just above it, due to solar heating. Therefore the lowest atmospheric layer absorbs heat from the ground, expands, and rises, producing the worst turbulence.

5.2 COMPUTATIONAL METHODS

5.2.1 A Simple Visible Algorithm

The visible band of wavelengths is narrow enough so that the L and E in (5.6) through (5.10) are usually considered to be luminance and illuminance, respectively, and not spectral functions. Also, in accordance with the preceding discussion, we assume only scattering plays any part in attenuating visible radiation, so $\tau = \tau_s = \exp(-\beta_s R)$.

5.2.1.1 Contrast

A crucial quantity that determines the ability of the human eye to detect is contrast between the target and the background against which it is seen. We define contrast as the difference in luminance between the target and background divided by the luminance of the background:

$$C \equiv \frac{L_T - L_B}{L_B} = L_T/L_B - 1 \qquad (5.11)$$

Note that the value of contrast can range from ∞, when the background is negligible compared to the target, to -1 when the target is negligible compared to the background. Zero contrast always means equal target and background luminances. If the luminances of (5.11) are measured close to the sources, so that there is negligible atmospheric effect, then the contrast is called inherent contrast, and is written C_0.

Contrast Reduction by the Atmosphere. At some appreciable range from the target, contrast would be given by

$$C = \frac{L_T(R) - L_B(R)}{L_B(R)} \tag{5.12}$$

Now if we simply used (5.8) for radiance and the target and background were at the same distance, each quantity on the right of (5.12) would be an L multiplied by the same value of τ, and the values of τ would cancel out. The net result would be as if we had used radiances measured close to the sources, so we would obtain $C = C_0$. We all know from experience that this result is wrong: long atmospheric paths tend to reduce the contrast to 0. The problem is that we are not including in-scattering; we must use (5.9) instead of (5.8) for both the target and background radiance. In doing so we interpret $\tau(R)$ and L_{is} for both target and background as pertaining to the range from *target* to sensor. Then L on the right-hand side of (5.9) for the background is the radiance of the background as seen from the target position. Using (5.9) in the numerator of (5.12) gives

$$C = \frac{(L_T - L_B) \exp(-\beta_s R)}{L_B(R)} = [L_B/L_B(R)] C_0 \exp(-\beta_s R) \tag{5.13}$$

Equation (5.13) is the most general form of the law for contrast reduction by the atmosphere and appears much like an exponential reduction of the inherent contrast except for the factor in front, which is the ratio of the background radiance from the target position to the background radiance from the sensor position. This result can reduce to exactly an exponential decay of the inherent contrast for one special geometry. If the target is viewed against the horizon sky then both L_B and $L_B(R)$ represent the luminance of the horizon sky (in the direction of the target), and (5.13) becomes

$$C = C_0 \exp(-\beta_s R) \tag{5.14}$$

We may also assume the same holds true for targets at reasonable ranges at higher altitudes viewed against the sky.

It is important to remember that (5.14) is not true for targets viewed against a terrestrial background. In that case a considerably more involved line of reasoning from Middleton [1] leads to

$$C = C_0\{1 - S[1 - \exp(\beta_s R)]\}^{-1} \qquad (5.15)$$

with

$$S \equiv L_m/L_B \qquad (5.16)$$

where

L_B = background radiance as seen from target position
L_m = horizon sky radiance from a certain direction.

The quantity S is called the *sky-ground ratio*. The direction from which L_m must be measured is such that sunlight is scattered from that direction toward the sensor at the same angle that it is scattered along the line of sight from the target (there are in general two such directions for any target-sensor-sun configuration). Figure 5.4 shows how contrast reduction depends on S. The sky-ground ratio would be very difficult to measure or calculate from the definition, but there is a rough approximation [1] that is quite easy to calculate:

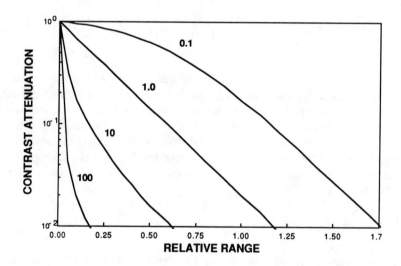

Figure 5.4 Contrast attenuation *versus* relative range with sky-ground ratio as a parameter.

$$S \approx \rho^{-1}, \quad \text{overcast sky} \tag{5.16a}$$

$$S \approx .2\rho^{-1}, \quad \text{clear sky} \tag{5.16b}$$

where ρ is the reflectance of the background. The values in Table 5.2 confirm this relationship.

Alteration of Luminance. The in-scattered radiance term of equation (5.9) may be calculated in a similar manner as contrast. In fact, by setting C on the left of (5.15) equal to its defining expression (5.12), we obtain

$$\frac{L_T(R) - L_B(R)}{L_B(R)} = C_0\{1 - S[1 - \exp(\beta_s R)]\}^{-1}$$

Then using (5.9) to substitute for the radiances on the left, and solving for L_{is}, gives

$$L_{\text{is}} = \tau L_B(C_0/C - 1) \tag{5.17}$$

When this is used in the expression for $L_B(R)$ (remember that L_B means the background luminance seen from the target position, which is at zero range if the background and target are at the same distance), we obtain

$$L_B(R) = \tau L_B C_0/C \tag{5.18}$$

Equation (5.18) is a mathematical expression of the fact that the background radiance, as seen by the sensor, approaches the horizon sky luminance at very long ranges. It does *not* approach 0, which is a common misconception, and the in-scattered radiance is precisely the reason it does not. This equation along with (5.15) describe atmospheric effects fairly completely in the visible region.

Table 5.2
Typical Values of the Sky-Ground
Ratio

Ground/Sky	Clear	Overcast
Fresh snow	0.2	1
Desert	1.4	7
Forest	5	25

5.2.1.2 Visibility

At this point our atmospheric formulas depend on the scattering coefficient, which itself can be quite difficult to calculate for a general case of Mie scattering. Here again a simple empirically measured quantity can be of great use by replacing β_s. The quantity of interest is called *visual range, meteorological range,* or *visibility.* We use all these terms synonymously in this treatment.

We may consider visibility to be roughly the range at which a black object can be seen against the horizon sky, assuming that the object is large enough so that size is not a limiting factor. The inherent contrast of such a target is -1. From (5.14) it can be seen that this contrast should approach 0 as the black target is moved farther and farther away. When the contrast is reduced to the threshold contrast of the eye (to be discussed in a later chapter), the object is just visible to the observer. The value of the threshold contrast that has been conventionally used since 1924 is 2% ($\pm$), although later investigations have resulted in slightly different values. Then (5.14) becomes

$$.02 = \exp(-\beta_s V)$$

where V is the visual range or visibility. So

$$\beta_s = 3.912/V \qquad\qquad (5.19)$$

This relationship is illustrated in Figure 5.5.

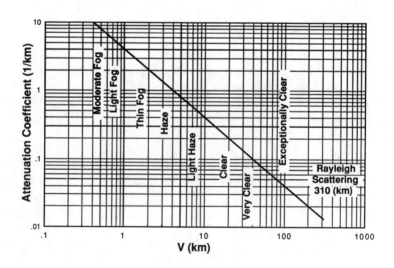

Figure 5.5 Visible attenuation coefficient *versus* visibility.

Because visibility is a meteorological variable commonly recorded by weather stations, it will serve as a convenient substitute for the scattering coefficient. We may express the atmospheric transmittance or contrast reduction in terms of V.

$$\tau = \exp(-3.912 R/V) \tag{5.20}$$

$$C = [L_B/L_B(R)]c_0 \exp(-3.912 R/V), \quad \text{general} \tag{5.21}$$

$$C = C_0 \exp(-3.912 R/V), \quad \text{sky background} \tag{5.22}$$

$$C = C_0\{1 - S[1 - \exp(3.912 R/V)]\}^{-1}, \quad \text{terrain background} \tag{5.23}$$

5.2.2 UVTRAN

One problem with the algorithm of Section 5.2.1 is in the assumption of no spectral dependence. Such an assumption rules out any treatment of color and any subtle interactions between the atmosphere and the scene spectral radiance. We may treat such spectral effects with the aid of computer models that are now available to give spectral transmittance. Later in this chapter we will discuss the computer model LOWTRAN, which is usually used in the IR range but also extends through the visible range. Here we wish to introduce the reader to a more recent, smaller, faster model designed just for the ultraviolet and visible regions: UVTRAN.

UVTRAN is a transmission model applicable between 185 and 700 nm, considering aerosol attenuation, molecular scattering, and molecular absorption. Note that the last process was ignored in the simple algorithm earlier. For its molecular absorption calculation, the model uses default values of molecular concentrations from the 1976 U.S. Standard Atmosphere; the user may change these during the input. On the other hand, its aerosol scattering calculation is practically identical with that described later in the section on empirical IR scattering and is parameterized by the one input variable of visibility.

The program is very quick and easy to use, requiring only the input to specify the path geometry, the visibility, and the wavelengths desired. It is available in PC version from the U.S. Army Atmospheric Sciences Laboratory in White Sands, New Mexico, for qualified users.

5.2.3 Empirical Method for IR Extinction

A simple empirical method [2] for calculating IR extinction was commonly used prior to the wide-scale dissemination of computer models for atmospheric effects. This method divides the IR spectrum up into eight windows, as shown in Figure 5.6. Then absorption and scattering are calculated separately for each window of

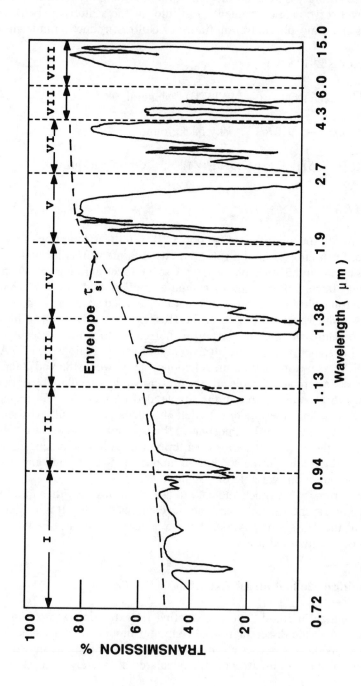

Figure 5.6 Windows for empirical IR atmospheric attenuation.

interest, using empirical formulas. The total transmittance is the product of scattering and absorption transmittance: $\tau = \tau_s \tau_a$.

5.2.3.1 Empirical IR Absorption

The point of view is adopted that the only variable component in atmospheric absorption is the amount of water vapor. Other gases that may absorb in the IR range remain fairly constant in concentration and therefore can have their effects incorporated in the constants of the algorithm. The crucial variable then is the precipitable mm (pr. mm) of water in the optical path, a function of air temperature, relative humidity, and range. The pr. mm of water means the thickness of the liquid column that would result if all the water in the path were condensed at one end of that path. The dependence of pr. mm of water on air temperature and relative humidity is shown in Figure 5.7. We need only multiply the values from the graph by range in km to get pr. cm of water and by 10 to convert from cm to pr. mm, W.

Alternatively, if the algorithm is to be put on computer, the following empirical equations may be used to get W:

$$x \equiv 273/T_A \tag{5.24}$$

$$W = .01 \cdot RH \cdot x \cdot R \cdot \exp(18.9766 - 14.9545x - 2.4388x^2) \tag{5.25}$$

where

T_A = air temperature in K
RH = relative humidity in %
R = range in km.

The empirical expressions for absorption transmissivity in the ith window at sea level are

$$\tau_{ai} = \exp(-A_i W^{1/2}), \quad W < W_i \tag{5.26a}$$

$$\tau_{ai} = k_i(W_i/W)^{\beta_i}, \quad W > W_i \tag{5.26b}$$

which are to be used with Table 5.3.

If not at sea level the transmissivity for a horizontal path can be approximated by

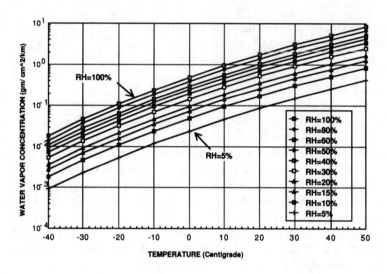

Figure 5.7 Water vapor concentration per km *versus* air temperature with relative humidity as a parameter.

Table 5.3
Constants for Empirical IR Absorption

Window	A_i	k_i	β_i	W_i
I	0.0305	0.800	0.112	54
II	0.0363	0.765	0.134	54
III	0.1303	0.830	0.093	2.0
IV	0.211	0.802	0.111	1.1
V	0.350	0.814	0.1035	.35
VI	0.373	0.827	0.095	.26
VII	0.913	0.679	0.194	.18
VIII	0.598	0.784	0.122	.165

$$\tau_{ai}(h) = \tau_{ai}(\text{sea level}) \left[\frac{P(\text{sea level})}{P(h)} \right]^{.25} \tag{5.27}$$

where

h = altitude of horizontal path
P = atmospheric pressure.

Slant paths would obviously be much more difficult, requiring some averaging process.

5.2.3.2 Empirical IR Scattering

From our earlier definitions we can write one for the scattering transmissivity in the ith window as approximately

$$\tau_{si} = \exp[-\beta_s(\lambda_i)R] \tag{5.28}$$

where λ_i is the center wavelength of ith window.

For Rayleigh scattering only, we know

$$\beta_s(\lambda)\alpha\lambda^{-4} \tag{5.29}$$

However, pure Rayleigh scattering would represent very little loss. The main problem in IR scattering stems from the aerosol: larger particles are suspended in the atmosphere. Our empirical scattering approach assumes a similar form for β_s in Mie scattering:

$$\beta_s(\lambda) = A\lambda^{-q} \tag{5.30}$$

with A and q to be determined by empirical data. We do know that, as the scattering particles get larger (approaching the wavelength of the radiation), there is less of a dependence on λ, so we expect $q < 4$. Also the scattering gets worse so we can relate particle size to the visibility parameter introduced in Section 5.2.1: high visibility implies a large q and the inverse also holds.

Some measurements [1] that we might note include $q = 2.09$ at $V \approx 150$ km, $q = 1.6$ at $V \approx 90$ km, and $q = 1.3$ at $V \approx 30$ km. For the lower visibilities typical of haze the following relation has been established for V in km:

$$q = .585V^{1/3} \tag{5.31}$$

The first three points roughly fit the straight line

$$q = 6.583 \times 10^{-3}V + 1.07 \tag{5.32}$$

This line merges with the function in (5.31) at $V = 7$ km, so we can use (5.31) for $V < 7$ km and (5.32) for $V > 7$ km.

Now we saw in the visible range that $\beta_s = 3.912/V$ so (5.30) at the middle of the visible band (.55 μm) becomes

$$\beta_s = A(.55)^{-q} = 3.912/V$$

or

$$A = (3.912/V) \cdot .55^q \tag{5.33}$$

Then at IR wavelengths

$$\beta_s = \frac{3.91}{V}\left(\frac{.55}{\lambda}\right)^q \tag{5.34}$$

$$\tau_{si} = \exp\left[-\frac{3.91}{V}\left(\frac{.55}{\lambda_i}\right)^q R\right] \tag{5.35}$$

In this algorithm, V first establishes q and then τ_{si} is calculated from (5.35). The main drawback to this approach is that wavelength dependence is determined totally from data in the visible region and probably becomes less and less reliable the farther away one gets into IR. However the atmosphere is characterized totally by T_A, RH, and V, three meteorological variables commonly reported; and such simplicity has much to recommend it.

5.2.3.3 Example of Empirical Method

Suppose we wish to find the transmittance for 2.7–4.3 μm radiation through 5 km of an atmosphere at sea level characterized by a temperature of 25 °C, a relative humidity of 70%, and a visibility of 3 km.

First a glance at Figure 5.6 tells us we are working in window VI. To find absorption we must find precipitable mm of water in the path. We could do this approximately from the graph of Figure 5.7, but instead we will illustrate the use of (5.24) and (5.25). We have $T_A = 298$ K and $x = .9161$, therefore from (5.25) $W = 81.1$ mm of H_2O. Next, inspection of Table 5.3 tells us that $W > W_i$ for window VI, so $\tau_a = .827(.26/81.1)^{.095} = .479$.

Next, we find q for scattering from (5.29): $q = .585 \times 3^{1/3} = .844$. Then (5.33) gives

$$\tau_s = \exp\left[-\frac{3.91}{3}\left(\frac{.55}{3.5}\right)^{.844} \times 5\right] = .255.$$

We can see that the algorithm predicts scattering to be significantly worse than absorption under these conditions. We combine the two to get $\tau = .479 \times .255 = .122$.

5.2.4 LOWTRAN

In the early 1970s the Air Force Geophysics Laboratory at Hanscom AFB in Massachusetts constructed a definitive model of atmospheric effects on electromagnetic radiation in the wavelength range .25–28 μm. Obviously the model could be used for the visible range also. Extinction and emission both were considered. At first the results were expressed in a set of charts and graphs [3] from which transmission through the atmosphere at low spectral resolution could be calculated. Because the resolution was too low to accurately predict transmission for the specific wavelengths of lasers, additional tables were provided for the most commonly used lasers.

Eventually their work grew into the computer models LOWTRAN (low spectral resolution) and HITRAN (high spectral resolution). LOWTRAN is now in its seventh version (LOWTRAN 7) and may be purchased in a PC version from ONTAR Corporation, Brookline, Massachusetts.

Basically LOWTRAN contains a number of model atmospheres, stratified into 1 km layers up to 25 km above sea level and into thicker layers from 25 to 100 km. These may be combined with a number of aerosol models. LOWTRAN 6 has 6 atmospheres and 8 aerosols, allowing 48 combinations to match the situation being modeled. In addition the user can define an atmosphere to be used.

Absorption transmissivity through these atmospheres is calculated using a band model that assumes an array of absorption lines within a spectral band, which have specified shapes, intensities, and spacing. The last three variables are adjusted to approximate the actual case within the spectral band of interest, and the results are averaged over the band. As has been common in spectroscopy, wavenumber instead of wavelength is used by the authors of LOWTRAN. Wavenumber, k, is defined as

$$k \equiv 1/\lambda \tag{5.36}$$

Usually k is expressed in cm^{-1} whereas λ is in μm. In this case

$$k = 10^4/\lambda \tag{5.37}$$

LOWTRAN uses bands of 20 cm^{-1} in wavenumber. Therefore the bands vary in size across the spectrum when expressed in wavelength, because

$$|dk| = (10^4/\lambda^2)\,d\lambda \tag{5.38}$$

The model is said to have a spectral resolution of 20 cm^{-1}. Transmittance accuracy is claimed to be ±5%.

Scattering transmittance is calculated from the number and size distribution of the particles in the chosen aerosol, using the Mie formulation. Then the two transmittances can be multiplied together to obtain the total transmittance. Furthermore, by calculating layer by layer and multiplying, slant paths can be accommodated. Additionally LOWTRAN will calculate atmospheric radiance along these paths. For details of use the reader is referred to the user's guide [4].

5.2.4.1 Prediction Charts

If we lack access to the computer model LOWTRAN, the same results may be achieved, albeit somewhat tediously, by using the early prediction charts. In this early stage the model only had five atmospheres and two aerosols. The atmospheres are Tropical, Midlatitude Summer, Midlatitude Winter, Subarctic Summer, Subarctic Winter. Aerosols are clear ($V = 25$ km) and hazy ($V = 5$ km).

The first 14 graphs used in this procedure allow us to ascertain the equivalent sea level path in each of the seven attenuating components of the atmosphere. Here is where the geometry of the scenario enters: there are two charts for each component (H_2O, O_3, uniformly mixed gases, *et cetera*), one chart is to be used for horizontal paths and the other for slant paths [3].

The charts for horizontal paths, all with variables subscripted h on the ordinate, may be used directly with range to get the equivalent sea level path length: multiply the graph reading for the appropriate altitude and atmospheric model by the range in km. For example, for pr. mm of water

$$W = w_h R \tag{5.39}$$

For a slant path from altitude z all the way through the atmosphere at zenith angle θ, just use the reading $w_v(z)$ in

$$W = w_v(z) \sec \theta \tag{5.40}$$

For a slant path from altitude z_1 to altitude z_2, use two readings from the w_v graph:

$$W = [w_v(z_1) - w_v(z_2)] \frac{R}{z_1 - z_2} \tag{5.41}$$

Using these methods we must calculate the equivalent sea level path for each of the seven components on the charts.

Each of the seven attenuating components is also represented on one or two transmittance prediction charts, along with transmittance and attenuator amount scales on adjacent sides of a vertical pointer. Two charts are sometimes used for one attenuating component in order to cover a wider spectral range [3]. Along with each of these charts we must use a separate transparency of the transmittance scale and pointer. Keeping the pointer on the transparency vertical, move it horizontally across the prediction chart of the attenuator of interest until it lines up with the wavelength (below) or wavenumber (above) of interest. Now adjust the transparency vertically on the prediction chart until the equivalent sea level amount (found from the first set of charts) on the right-hand scale (marked *scaling factor*) of the pointer aligns with the horizontal reference line running across the prediction chart. With this horizontal and vertical alignment of the pointer, we can then read the transmittance scale on the left side of the pointer, where the curve on the prediction chart crosses. This procedure should be followed for each wavelength of concern for each attenuator of the atmosphere. At a single wavelength the seven transmittances so found may then be multiplied together to give the total transmittance.

5.2.4.2 Laser Wavelengths

To supplement the prediction charts, there are tables of attenuation coefficients of the 5 model atmospheres and 2 model aerosols for the 12 specific lasers of Table 5.4 [3].

Table 5.4
Laser Wavelengths

Type	Wavelength (μm)
Nitrogen	0.3371
Argon	0.4880
Argon	0.5145
Helium-neon	0.6328
Ruby	0.6943
Gallium arsenide	0.86
Neodymium in glass	1.06
Erbium in glass	1.536
Helium-neon	3.39225
Carbon dioxide	10.591
Water vapor	27.9
Hydrogen cyanide	337

5.2.5 HITRAN and FASCODE

Models of atmospheric effects with much higher spectral resolution than LOW-TRAN have been developed by using detailed, line-by-line spectroscopic calculations. The earliest, HITRAN, was developed concurrently with LOWTRAN, but required much greater computer time and has never been developed into a flexible, system-oriented code like LOWTRAN.

New and faster methods of line-by-line calculations have resulted in the computer code FASCODE, from the same lab that produced LOWTRAN and HITRAN. FASCODE is unlikely to be needed for most system work. One exception might be laser calculations at wavelengths not included in Table 5.4. The potential user is referred to the user's manual [5].

5.2.6 EOSAEL

Once LOWTRAN became available other computer models, more specifically designed to simulate tactical battlefield situations, could be built around it. Such is the case for EOSAEL (electro-optical systems atmospheric effects library) designed by the U.S. Army Atmospheric Sciences Laboratory at White Sands, New Mexico. The heart of the EOSAEL collection of models is a trimmed-down version of LOWTRAN 4 to calculate transmittance and radiance of the natural atmosphere. However, EOSAEL proceeds from there to offer many different modules for calculating the effects of battlefield-induced contaminants like smoke (from a menu of over 20 screening smoke munitions), high-explosive dust, and vehicular dust. Various other modules are concerned with the effects of turbulence and absorption on laser beams, backscatter of lasers, effects of clouds, precipitation, and so forth. These modules are outlined in Table 5.5.

5.2.7 Precipitation

The presence of precipitation falling through the air increases the scattering of electromagnetic radiation over and above that due to the gases and aerosols. Fortunately this additional scattering is very nearly independent of wavelength because the scattering particles are very large compared to either visible or IR wavelengths: we are in the geometrical optics regime for both spectral bands. However the amount of scattering will depend on the density and size distribution of the particles.

5.2.7.1 Rain

There is apparently a connection between the rain rate and the size distribution of the raindrops. Happily this fact allows us to formulate an empirical relation

Table 5.5
EOSAEL Modules

Subject	Name	Range (μm)	Calculates
Gases	LT4M	.25–2, 3–5, 8–12	Transmission and radiance
	LZTRAN	.55–11	Transmission of specific laser wavelengths
	NMMW	10–1000 GHz	Transmission, backscatter and refraction
Natural aerosols	XSCALE	1.06, 3–5, 8–12	Transmission for slant or horizontal paths
	CLIMAT		Meteorological parameters for select locations
	CLTRAN	.2–2, 3–5, 8–12	Slant path transmission through six cloud types
Battlefield aerosols	COMBIC	.4–1.2, 3–5, 8–12, 94 GHz	Transmission, path length through smoke, dust
	SCREEN		Smoke munitions necessary for given screening
	GRNADE	.4–.7, .7–1.2, 3–5, 8–12, 1.06, 10.6, 94 GHz	Obscuration from tube launched grenades for self-screening
	FITTE	.4–14	Transmission through fire smoke
	MPLUME		Performance degradation due to missile smoke
Radiative transfer	SPOT	.25–2, 3–5, 8–12	Radiative energy reaching a detector
	FCLOUD	Any λ	Beam transmission, path radiance, contrast transmission through clouds
	OVRCST	Any λ	Beam transmission, path radiance, contrast transmission under overcast sky
	MSCAT	Any λ	Multiple scattering of laser beam in clouds
	TURB	< 14 μm	Laser spot size, jitter, scintillation at target
	BRLPRO	< 14 μm	Clear air, linear and nonlinear effects on high-energy laser beams

between the scattering coefficient in km^{-1} and the single variable of rain rate. The Gilbertson algorithm [6] is commonly used:

$$\beta_s = .248 \, r^{.67} \qquad (5.42)$$

where r is the rain rate in mm/hr.

A more recent article [7] finds a slightly different empirical relation for scattering at 10.6 μm and lists results from two other investigators as well. These three relations are

$$\beta_s = .322 \, r^{.6} \qquad (5.43)$$

$$\beta_s = .249 r^{.659} \tag{5.44}$$

$$\beta_s = .423 r^{.501} \tag{5.45}$$

However all four formulas give answers so close together for rates up to 30 mm/hr, that it does not really matter which one is used. Comparison of the algorithms is shown in Figure 5.8.

5.2.7.2 Snow

The size distribution of snowflakes is not related to the precipitation rate as simply. The rate of snow accumulation is usually expressed as equivalent liquid water rate in mm/hr. The great variety in types of snow crystals seems to rule out any single, simple relation between this variable and extinction coefficient. Experimental results [8] do tend to show two general groupings: one for small, needle-shaped crystals; and the other for larger, platelike crystals. The two relations fitting these are, respectively,

$$\beta_s = 3.2 r^{.91} \tag{5.46}$$

$$\beta_s = 1.3 r^{.5} \tag{5.47}$$

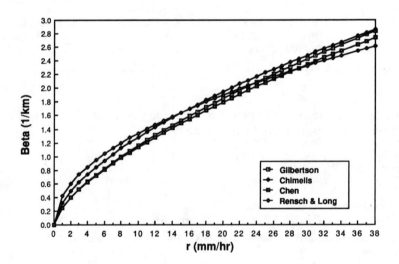

Figure 5.8 Comparison of rain algorithm.

5.2.8 Turbulence

The discussion of Section 5.1.3 noted that atmospheric turbulence will tend to blur the image and small details will suffer more than large ones. Such a type of degradation is often characterized by a modulation transfer function. The full explanation of this concept is undertaken in the next chapter. For our purposes here we may very roughly describe MTF as a function of spatial frequency that gives the reduction in contrast to that size detail. Large details in the image have low spatial frequencies whereas small ones have high spatial frequencies, so we expect the MTF to be a monotonically decreasing function of spatial frequency. MTF just multiplies the contrast so it starts (at zero frequency) at unity and decreases toward 0 as the spatial frequency approaches that of the smallest detail that can be seen.

The MTF of a turbulent atmosphere can be expressed in terms of a parameter called the *coherence diameter* or *coherence distance*, r_0. This is the lateral (perpendicular to the direction of propagation) distance over which the radiation from a point source remains coherent, or essentially undisrupted by the turbulence. It is also roughly equal to the diameter of a diffraction-limited optical system with the same resolution as that permitted by the turbulence. In terms of r_0

$$\text{MTF}_A = \exp[-3.44(\lambda \nu_s/r_0)^{5/3}] \tag{5.48}$$

where

λ = wavelength
ν_s = spatial frequency in cycles/rad.

The main problem in modeling turbulence comes in trying to relate r_0 to measured and reported properties of the atmosphere. Generally, the coherence distance is related to another descriptor of the turbulent atmosphere: the refractive index structure parameter [9], C_n^2.

$$r_0^{-5/3} = .4233 k^2 \int_0^L C_n^2(z)(z/L)^{5/3} dz \tag{5.49}$$

where

$k = 2\pi/\lambda$
z = altitude
L = path length in the turbulence.

The index structure parameter is defined as the variance in the refractive index, n, divided by the 2/3 power of distance, d, over which the variance is calculated:

$$C_n^2 \equiv \mathrm{var}(n)/d^{2/3} \tag{5.50}$$

Note that equation (5.49) implies that C_n^2 is typically a function of altitude. In the common case of a horizontal path, C_n^2 may be removed from the integral, and (5.49) simplifies to

$$r_0^{-5/3} = .1587 k^2 C_n^2 L \tag{5.51}$$

A great many experimental studies try to relate the value of the index structure parameter to the measurable environment. The empirical relations become quite complicated and require the evaluation of many factors, such as solar elevation angle, terrain type, and wind. The details are too lengthy to include here, but the best reference source is probably *The Infrared Handbook* [9]. Once a value is found for C_n^2, it leads directly to an MTF through equations (5.49) and (5.48). Figure 5.9 shows measured values of C_n^2 2 m above a grassy surface.

5.3 OVERVIEW OF ATMOSPHERIC MODELING

The modeling of atmospherics is quite mature compared to most aspects of electro-optical system modeling. Furthermore, with the continuing refinement and release of updated versions of LOWTRAN by the USAF Geophysical Laboratory and EOSAEL by the U.S. Army Atmospheric Sciences Laboratory, such is likely to remain the case for the foreseeable future. The systems modeler is therefore in the fortunate position of being able to choose the atmospheric model suitable to the needs at hand as a finished package.

The one area where we (the authors) have seen an unfulfilled need is in a parametric, statistical BIC model. The EOSAEL modules dealing with BIC all have very specific geometries, with munitions detonation or dust clouds originating at specified locations relative to lines of sight, winds, and so on. However, in operations research it is often more useful to have a statistical description of the BIC effects, perhaps related to more general battlefield conditions, such as length of battle, numbers and types of weapons employed, and so forth. At present, such questions can be approached only by averaging the output from many EOSAEL runs for slightly different scenarios.

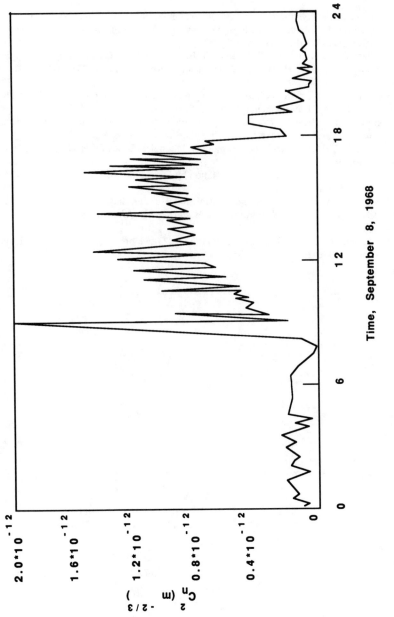

Figure 5.9 Refractive index structure parameter *versus* time of day, 2 m above a grassy plain. (Courtesy of R. S. Lawrence, G. R. Ochs, and S.F. Clifford, "Measurement of Atmospheric Turbulence Relevant to Optical Propagation," *J. Opt. Soc. Am.*, Vol. 60, No. 6, 1970, pp. 826–830.)

REFERENCES

1. W.E.K. Middleton, *Vision through the Atmosphere*, University of Toronto Press, Toronto, 1952.
2. P.W. Kruse, L.D. McLaughlin, and R.B. McQuistan, *Elements of Infrared Technology*, John Wiley and Sons, New York, 1963, pp. 172–192.
3. R.A. McClatchey, R.W. Fenn, J.E.A. Selby, F.E. Volz, and J.S. Garing, "Optical Properties of the Atmosphere," AFCRL-71-0279, Environmental Research Paper 354, AD 726116, May 10, 1971.
4. R.A. McClatchey *et al.*, "Atmospheric Transmittance/Radiance: Computer Code LOWTRAN 5" AFGL-TR-80-0067, Environmental Research Paper 897, February 21, 1980.
5. H.J.P. Smith *et al.*, "FASCODE—Fast Atmospheric Signature Code (Spectral Transmittance and Radiance)," AFGL-TR-78-0081, AD A057506, January 16, 1978.
6. RCA Corporation, *RCA Electro-Optics Handbook*, Technical Series EOH-11, Solid State Div., Lancaster, Pa., 1974, p. 87.
7. V. Chimelisx, "Extinction of CO_2 Laser Radiation by Fog and Rain," *Appl. Opt.*, Vol. 21, No. 18, September 15, 1982, p. 3367.
8. M.A. Seagraves, "Visible and Infrared Transmission Through Snow," *SPIE Proc. on Atmospheric Effects on Electro-Optical, Infrared, and Millimeter Wave Systems Performance*, Vol. 305, August 1981.
9. W.L. Wolfe and G.J. Zissis, *The Infrared Handbook*, Office of Naval Research, Washington, DC, 1978, pp. 6–20–6–29.

Chapter 6
System Modeling

6.1 OVERVIEW

Thus far in this book we have dealt with the generation of an intrinsic contrast signature of a target to its background, and we have followed that signature's degradation as it propagates through the atmosphere to the basic detector. In this chapter we will deal with how to mathematically describe the operation of the electro-optical system, be it a FLIR system, working in the infrared band, or a TV system operating in the visible band.

Whether it is a FLIR or a TV system that we intend to model, it will have the same basic elements:

1. Optics
2. Scanning
3. Detectors
4. Electronics
5. Display.

And whereas there are differences between how TV and FLIR systems are modeled, any mathematical model should address this common list.

The optical component of any EO system acts as a gatherer of the radiant energy and often acts as a spectral bandpass filter to enhance the signal-to-noise ratio or the target-to-background contrast ratio. The optical system then focuses the radiant energy onto the detector. In infrared systems of today, it is more usual to scan the scene onto a small number of detectors sequentially. The detectors convert the visual or infrared energy into electrons. These electrons are processed and amplified, and then used to drive a display which produces a visual picture of the viewed scene. In the early FLIR systems, once the infrared detector output had been processed and amplified, its output was used to modulate a *light emitting diode* (LED). The infrared scene as viewed by one detector gave a corresponding—

---

spatially one for one—visual intensity from the output of the LED. Such a system component was known as an *electro-optical multiplexer* (EOMUX) and obviated the need for a cathode ray tube.

Whatever type of display is used to present the image to the human being, the overall process results in a change of signature both in size (or magnification) and contrast as presented to the eye. Any analysis must be capable of describing from a total system perspective the change in size and contrast of the image from that received into the entrance aperture of the electro-optical system to that displayed to the human observer.

In the following chapter, we will deal briefly with an understanding of linear systems and how that technology may be used to analyze TV and infrared systems. We will next cover the analysis of the optical subcomponent; then we will review the electronic subcomponent including the scanning element, the detector, and the signal processing; and finally we will describe the display subcomponent of the system.

6.1.1 Linear Systems

It seems evident that when trying to view small objects (i.e., objects of small angular substance, whether because of their physical size or extremes of observation range) detection is aided by optimal magnification. The more the magnification, the larger the image and, correspondingly, the easier it is to detect and recognize the object. If one could continue to magnify the image, it would seem evident that there would be no end to this process. Unfortunately, our simplistic view of the world is interrupted by reality, and there comes a point in this continual magnification whereupon the magnifying system is no longer able to map any given point in the object plane to a unique point on the image plane. The radiant energy from a point in the object plane is blurred into an area in the image plane. Adjacent, resolvable points in the object plane become merged and we lose image quality. Greater magnification further merges and blends these adjacent points and the sharpness of contrast of the original image is accordingly diffused. Further magnification is therefore regarded as "empty magnification" in that it may yield a spatially larger image but with losses in contrast and image quality.

Human detection is predicated on size, contrast, and image quality, so it is necessary to find a method for taking account of all of these. The single most useful (and irreplaceable) tool for design, analysis, and specification is the transfer function methodology, as it links spatial resolution to contrast effects. This transfer function methodology yields such parameters as *optical transfer function* (OTF) and *contrast transfer function* (CTF). A formal definition of these is given in this chapter, where we will also (1) introduce the origins of linear filter theory; (2) provide an understanding of the theory of convolution; the Fourier transforms, and their application to optical system analysis; (3) indicate when it is safe to use such a tool and, perhaps more important, when it is not; and (4) give examples of common OTFs and CTFs.

As stated earlier, most electro-optical systems and FLIR systems consist of four different component technologies: optical, electro-optical, mechanical (scanning), and electronic subelements. When the human views the final image, each part has had an impact to a varying degree on the overall image quality. What the system designer requires is a tool that allows modeling the total transfer relationship between a point in the image plane to the point in the displayed object plane. For many years, linear filter theory had been employed in servo mechanism analysis to model the relationship of the output to the input of the system. The parallels are so evident that the optical designers also look to linear filter theory to establish the relationship between input and output. There are some fundamental differences, however, in that, for optical systems, the image is essentially a two-dimensional projection of three-dimensional space. Rigorous analysis should in fact be four-dimensional, although it is often simplified to two dimensions because we are often more concerned with spatial-contrast relationships than temporal relationships.

As shown in Figure 6.1, we adopt a coordinate scheme and nomenclature. A point in object space is located by Cartesian angular coordinates (x_o and y_o) measured in the x and y directions between the optical pointing axis and the line

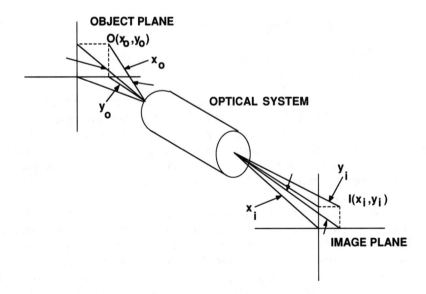

Figure 6.1 Geometry for electro-optical system analysis.

of sight from the aperture to the point. The image plane angular coordinates (x_i, y_i) are between the optical pointing axis and the line of sight from the exit of the optical systems to the point in image plane. For a distortionless system,

$$x_i = mx_o \tag{6.1a}$$

$$y_i = my_o \tag{6.1b}$$

where m is the angular magnification.

This is fine if the transfer unit is through one optical piece; however, in even the simplest FLIR system, there are optical components, scanners (i.e., mechanical components), detectors (i.e., electro-optical devices), filters or signal processing (i.e., electronic) components, and displays (both electro-optical and optical). We will see later, similar to the transfer function analysis methodology for servo mechanisms, that we can similarly cascade the optical transfer function of these individual elements to achieve the single optical transfer function of the system.

Let us now define the radiance exitance of the object as $o(x_o, y_o)$. The corresponding image distribution is $i(x_i, y_i)$. The imaging system may be thought of as an operator, **S**, where

$$i(x_i, y_i) = \mathbf{S} \cdot o(x_o, y_o) \tag{6.2}$$

or

$$\mathbf{S} = \frac{i(x_i, y_i)}{o(x_o, y_o)} \tag{6.3}$$

S is an arbitrary function that can be thought of as the transfer function of the optical system. Note its similarity in form to the transfer function of a servo mechanism, and note also the confusion of the nomenclature. Those familiar with servo theory think of the *o* and *i* subscripts as corresponding to output and input, whereas for optical transfer functions these refer to object and image planes, respectively. The object plane is the input, and the image plane is the output. This leads initially to a lot of confusion.

A slight digression here is worthwhile. We clearly see the parallels to circuit and servo analysis; however, there are two fundamental differences between circuit analysis and optical analysis, which stem from the fact that the former is a time filter whereas the latter is a spatial filter. Time filters are single sided and satisfy the causality requirement that no change in the output occurs before the application of an input. Optical filters, on the other hand, are double sided in space. For time filters we use the single-sided Laplace; for spatial filters we use the double-sided

Fourier transform. The second difference is that electrical signals may be either positive or negative. Optical intensities are always positive.

One final point of explanation as we are dealing with spatial filters; it is necessary to define spatial frequencies having units of cycles per milliradian. The definition is as shown in Figure 6.2. If a one-dimensional sinusoidally varying light source having a period θ_x is viewed at a distance R meters, then

$$\theta_x = \frac{T_x}{R \times 10^3} \text{ milliradians} \tag{6.4}$$

where T_x is the linear period and the spatial frequency, ν_x, is given by

$$\nu_x = 1/\theta_x = 10^3 R/T_x \text{ cycles/milliradian} \tag{6.5}$$

If **S** satisfies the conditions for linearity we can bring to bear the power of linear analysis. Furthermore, if we now cascade two or more optical stages, the image plane of one becomes the object plane of the next stage, and we may simply multiply the transfer functions to gain the overall transfer function of the overall system, as shown in Figure 6.3. The key to this is that they must be linear. A system is defined to be linear if, for arbitrary complex scalar weightings a and b of arbitrary object functions $o_1(x_o, y_o)$ and $o_2(x_o, y_o)$, the following equation is satisfied:

$$\mathbf{S}[ao_1(x_o, y_o) + bo_1(x_o, y_o)] = a\mathbf{S}[o_1(x_o, y_o)] + b\mathbf{S}[o_2(x_o, y_o)] \tag{6.6}$$

This equation implies that superposition holds true. As a consequence, any object function can be represented as a series or in the limit an integral of simpler functions. If this is the case then we can invoke the powerful tools already developed for linear analysis, in particular Fourier analysis. However, before we get too far ahead it is appropriate to refresh ourselves on convolution theory and, prior to this, on understanding certain key properties of the Dirac delta function.

6.1.2 Dirac Delta Functions

The one-dimensional Dirac delta function can be defined as the limit of a sequence of pulses of decreasing width, increasing height and unit area. The beauty of such a definition is that a multitude of different pulse shapes can be used in the definition; for example,

$$\delta(t) = \lim_{N \to \infty} N \exp(-N^2 \pi t^2) \tag{6.7}$$

$$\delta(t) = \lim_{N \to \infty} N \operatorname{rect}(Nt) \tag{6.8}$$

$$\delta(t) = \lim_{N \to \infty} N \operatorname{sinc}(Nt) \tag{6.9}$$

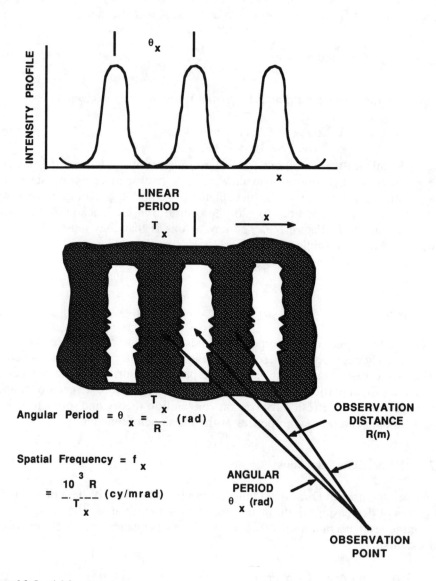

Figure 6.2 Spatial frequency.

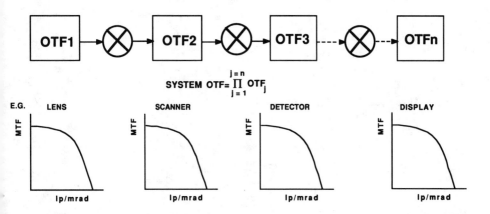

Figure 6.3 System transfer function from component transfer functions.

Although the one-dimensional delta function is used in circuit analysis, the analogous concept in optics is a spatial pulse of unit area (i.e., a point source of light). The corresponding definition of the Dirac delta function in two-dimensional space is a simple extension of the one-dimensional case with even greater latitude in the possible choice for the functional form; for example,

$$\delta(x, y) = \lim_{N\to\infty} N^2 \exp[-N^2 \pi (x^2 + y^2)] \tag{6.10}$$

$$\delta(x, y) = \lim_{N\to\infty} N^2 \operatorname{rect}(Nx) \operatorname{rect}(Ny) \tag{6.11}$$

$$\delta(x, y) = \lim_{N\to\infty} N^2 \operatorname{sinc}(Nx) \operatorname{sinc}(Ny) \tag{6.12}$$

$$\delta(x, y) = \lim_{N\to\infty} \frac{N^2}{\pi} \operatorname{circ}(N\sqrt{x^2 + y^2}) \tag{6.13}$$

$$\delta(x, y) = \lim_{N\to\infty} N \frac{J_1(2\pi N\sqrt{x^2 + y^2})}{\sqrt{x^2 + y^2}} \tag{6.14}$$

The first three of the preceding definitions are in rectangular coordinates, the last two are circularly symmetric. Each of these definitions of the spatial Dirac delta function has the following fundamental properties:

$$\delta(x, y) = \begin{cases} \infty, & x = y = 0 \\ 0, & \text{otherwise} \end{cases} \tag{6.15}$$

$$\int\int_{-\epsilon}^{\epsilon} \delta(x, y)\,dxdy = 1, \quad \text{any } \epsilon > 0 \tag{6.16}$$

$$\int\int_{-\infty}^{\infty} g(\xi, \eta)\delta(x - \xi, y - \eta)\,d\xi d\eta = g(x, y) \tag{6.17}$$

at each point of continuity of g.

This last property is often referred to as the *sifting property* of the Dirac function. Note that the variables in a two-dimensional delta function are separable, so that $\delta(x, y) = \delta(x)\delta(y)$. The sifting property can be applied to the mathematical description of our object distribution:

$$o(x_o, y_o) = \int\int_{-\infty}^{\infty} o(\xi, \eta)\delta(x_o - \xi)\delta(y_o - \eta)\,d\xi d\eta \tag{6.18}$$

Its geometric interpretation is shown in Figure 6.4. The arbitrary function can be represented as an infinite sum of weighted and displaced delta functions. The corresponding image distribution $i(x_i, y_i)$ is

$$i(x_i, y_i) = \mathbf{S}[o(x_o, y_o)] = \mathbf{S}\left[\int\int_{-\infty}^{\infty} o(\xi, \eta)\delta(x_o - \xi)\delta(y_o - \eta)\,d\xi d\eta\right] \tag{6.19}$$

If the system is linear, then

$$i(x_i, y_i) = \int\int_{-\infty}^{\infty} o(\xi, \eta)\mathbf{S}[\delta(x_o - \xi)\delta(y_o - \eta)]\,d\xi d\eta \tag{6.20}$$

This is an important equation. It can be interpreted that each element in the object plane $o(\xi, \eta)\,d\xi d\eta$ produces a patch of light $o(\xi, \eta)\mathbf{S}[\delta(x - \xi)\delta(y - \eta)]\,d\xi d\eta$ at the point (x, y). The image distribution is the summation due to all elements in the object plane. The preceding equation is known as the *superposition integral* and the term $\mathbf{S}[\delta(x_o - \xi)\delta(y_o - \eta)]$ is known as the *point spread function*.

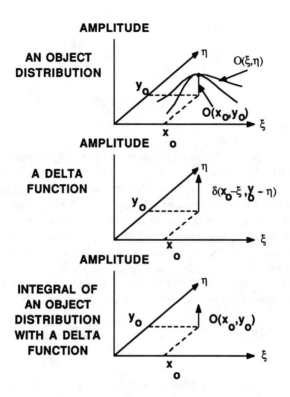

Figure 6.4 Sifting property of Dirac delta function.

Its name is very descriptive. It defines the way a point in object space is spread (or diffused) into image space. When we assess the quality of an optical system to produce a clear image, we really are investigating the "narrowness" of the point spread function.

As the linear imaging system is space invariant (or isoplanatic), that is, its point spread function depends only on the distances $(x_o - \xi)$ and $(y_o - \eta)$, we can recognize (6.20) as a two-dimensional convolution of the object function with the point spread function of the system. In practice, imaging systems are seldom isoplanatic over their object field, but it is usually possible to divide the object field into small regions known as *isoplanatic patches* within which the system is approximately invariant.

In Section 6.1.3 we will introduce the convolution properties of a Fourier transform, which are

$$\mathcal{F}[g(x, y)] = G(\nu_x, \nu_y) \tag{6.21a}$$

$$\mathscr{F}[h(x, y)] = H(\nu_x, \nu_y) \tag{6.21b}$$

then

$$\mathscr{F}\left[\int\int_{-\infty}^{\infty} o(\xi, \eta) s(x - \xi, y - \eta) d\xi d\eta\right] = O(\nu_x, \nu_y) S(\nu_x, \nu_y) \tag{6.22}$$

This simply states that the Fourier transform of the convolution of two functions equals the product of the two Fourier transforms of the individual functions.

Many authors on this subject point out that in the analysis of optical systems, object functions are four-dimensional functions of space and time. Although this is true, two of the dimensions add little into the insight of the analysis. The first dimension that is ignored in further analysis in this chapter is that of depth. For the analysis we will consider all object points to emanate from a single plane orthogonal to optical pointing axis. The second dimension to be ignored is that of time. We will assume for now that the object distribution does not change with time. We can always add the time history of the image later by

$$i(x_i, y_i, t) = \mathbf{S}[o(x_o, y_o, t)]$$

$$= \int\int\int_{-\infty}^{\infty} o(\xi, \eta, t') \mathbf{S}[\delta(x_o - \xi) \delta(y_o - \eta) \delta(t - t')] d\xi d\eta dt' \tag{6.23}$$

6.1.3 Fourier Transform

Taking the Fourier transform of the object distribution

$$\mathscr{F}[o(x, y)] \equiv \int\int_{-\infty}^{\infty} o(x, y) \exp[-2\pi(x\nu_x + y\nu_y)] dx dy \equiv O(\nu_x, \nu_y) \tag{6.24}$$

The inverse transform is

$$\mathscr{F}^{-1}[O(\nu_x, \nu_y)] \equiv \frac{1}{(2\pi)^2} \int\int_{-\infty}^{\infty} O(\nu_x, \nu_y) \exp[2\pi(x\nu_x + y\nu_y)] d\nu_x d\nu_y \tag{6.25}$$

Successive forward and inverse transformations yield the original function, that is

$$\mathcal{F}^{-1}\{\mathcal{F}[o(x, y)]\} = o(x, y) \tag{6.26}$$

As we studied earlier, the Fourier transform of the convolution of two functions equals the product of the transforms of the two functions. For the image equation of

$$i(x_i, y_i) = \int\limits_{-\infty}^{\infty}\int o(\xi, \eta)S[\delta(x_i - \xi)\delta(y_i - \eta)]d\xi d\eta$$

we will first define

$$S[\delta(x_i - \xi)\delta(y_i - \eta)] \equiv r(x_i, y_i) \tag{6.27}$$

then

$$i(x_i, y_i) = o(x_i, y_i) * r(x_i, y_i) \tag{6.28}$$

Taking the Fourier transform of the preceding yields

$$\mathcal{F}[i] = \mathcal{F}[o*r] = \mathcal{F}[o] \cdot \mathcal{F}[r] \tag{6.29}$$

An abbreviated notion for this is

$$I = O \cdot R \tag{6.30}$$

The Fourier transform R of an impulse response r is called the *optical transfer function*. For an optical system made from several components each with its own impulse (or point spread) responses, the total system impulse response r_S is produced by a series of convolutions,

$$r_S = r_1 * r_2 * \cdots * r_n \tag{6.31}$$

Then by the convolution theorem, the cascaded transfer function can be multiplied together to produce the system OTF:

$$R_S = \prod_{m=1}^{n} R_m \tag{6.32}$$

and the image spectrum is

$$I = O \prod_{m=1}^{n} R_m \tag{6.33}$$

This seems intuitively obvious to an engineer who is well versed in linear servo theory. Again, remember that this differs for optical systems in that the variable is space, not time. The result is that the complicated operation of multiple convolutions can be replaced by a simpler process of finding the inverse product of the convolved functions. The imaging process can therefore be thought to have an OTF that represents a selective weighting of the object's spatial frequency spectrum. This OTF is a measure of an imaging system's ability to recreate the spatial frequency content of a scene.

The OTF is a complex quantity whose modulus is a sine wave amplitude response function called the *modulation transfer function* and whose argument is called the *phase transfer function* (PTF).

$$\text{OTF}(\nu_x, \nu_y) \equiv \text{MTF}(\nu_x, \nu_y) \exp[j \, \text{PTF}(\nu_x, \nu_y)] \tag{6.34}$$

The concept that an optical system may be thought to possess an optical transfer function which weighs the spatial frequency of the input object to the output image is rather powerful. Further, that the total performance a total optical system composed of many subcomponents is obtained by multiplying the individual OTFs of the elements makes this form of analysis the most powerful tool for analyzing the image quality of a system.

6.1.4 Extensions to TV and FLIR Analysis

So far, we have talked mainly about pure optical systems. The concept discussed previously can be applied to a total TV or FLIR system, including the elements of optical magnification, scanner, detector, and display. Each part must be analyzed as it affects the spatial frequency domain, and then, assuming the original conditions hold, the total system response is the product of the individual spatial frequency responses or MTFs. These conditions, known as the *existence conditions*, are stated as

1. The radiation detection is incoherent.
2. The signal processing is linear.
3. The imaging is spatially invariant.
4. The system mapping is single valued (specifically nonnoisy).

The last three of these so-called existence conditions are regularly violated in FLIR system analyses.

FLIRs are not spatially invariant. Their response varies from the center of the field of view to the edge due to aberrations. Similarly, if the scan position is nonlinear, the response will not be spatially invariant. For instance, for a parallel scanning system, the detector array samples periodically in the direction perpendicular to the scan, thereby producing nonconvolutionary imagery. Further, each detector is noisy. The analog electronics may be both nonlinear and noisy. Sometimes signal compression is used to improve the dynamic response and often the electro-optical conversion of the display is nonlinear. All these factors would say that we are on shaky ground when we use MTFs to analyze FLIR systems. Nevertheless, it is still the most powerful method of predicting image quality, and as long as we are careful to account for (or avoid) these deviations from the existence conditions, we can use the MTF as a design, analysis, and specification tool.

In addition to the preceding deviations, there are some further nontrivial ways in which a FLIR system differs from other optical systems:

1. FLIRs usually are ac coupled; they subtract the average scene value from the video and display only variations around the average value; and they add an arbitrary constant to the display image.
2. Electronic signal shaping or special display techniques may be used to produce spread functions with negative amplitudes, producing MTFs with greater than unity amplitude. Such a step is taken to artificially boost the FLIR resolution at high spatial frequencies while sacrificing the system fidelity at low frequencies. This causes an MTF definition and normalization problem.
3. Many quasi-linear system operating points may be identified whose corresponding MTFs may not be identical.
4. The image may be formed by an insufficiently filtered sampling process so that the MTF exists only in the direction normal to the direction in which the sampling operates. (Note: An empirical study performed under Ratches at C^2NVEO established that the recognition probability stays roughly the same as long as horizontal and vertical resolutions stay within the ratio 1:2.)

The first of these differences is by far the most important; however, the second and fourth need a little further explanation. The second deals with an MTF that can apparently be greater than unity. From the passive case of optics it seems self-evident that, once an image quality has been destroyed by any point spread function, the subsequent image quality cannot be improved by adding optical stages. Once the energy from the original image has been spread it would seem evident that it either stays spread by the same amount or more by the next optical stage; it cannot be narrowed. The normalization process of MTFs for optical systems prohibits an MTF greater than unity. For active signal processing, which can yield spread functions with negative amplitudes, it is possible to produce compensating MTFs with amplitudes greater than unity.

The fourth difference is that most FLIRs do not satisfy the MTF existence requirements in all directions. It is often necessary to reduce the point spread function in a direction in which all conditions are satisfied. This results in the determination of a line spread function, which is the response to a long infinitely narrow line source composed of a string of delta functions. This contains spatial frequencies only in a direction perpendicular to the long dimension and contains all frequencies with unity amplitude from 0 to infinity (it is therefore unidirectional).

As the analog signal corresponding to this line passes through each component of the system, its frequency content is attenuated selectively. The image that appears at the output is not precisely reproduced, and the effect is the observed spreading of the line image.

Example curves of LSF and MTF for a FLIR are provided in Figure 6.5. The curves are dominated by the detector subtense α, so the x axis is normalized to α.

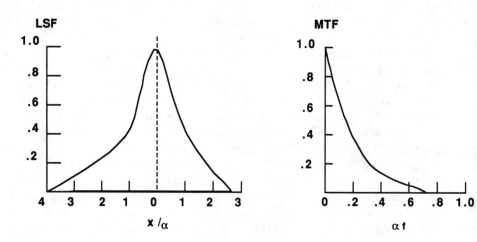

Figure 6.5 Examples of a FLIR LSF and MTF.

6.1.5   Frequently Used Functions and Useful Fourier Transform Pairs

Rectangle function:

$$\text{rect}(x) \equiv \begin{cases} 1 & |x| \leq 1/2 \\ 0 & \text{otherwise} \end{cases}$$

Sinc function:

$$\mathrm{sinc}\,(x) \equiv \frac{\sin{(\pi x)}}{\pi x}$$

Sign function:

$$\mathrm{sgn}\,(x) \equiv \begin{cases} 1 & x > 0 \\ 0 & x = 0 \\ -1 & x < 0 \end{cases}$$

Triangle function:

$$\triangle(x) \equiv \begin{cases} 1 - |x| & |x| \le 1 \\ 0 & \text{otherwise} \end{cases}$$

Comb function:

$$\mathrm{comb}\,(x) = \sum_{n=-\infty}^{\infty} \delta(x - n)$$

Circle function:

$$\mathrm{circ}\,(\sqrt{x^2 + y^2}) = \begin{cases} 1 & \sqrt{x^2 + y^2} \le 1 \\ 0 & \text{otherwise} \end{cases}$$

These are all one dimensional. Two-dimensional functions can be formed by products of these functions with the exception of circular functions. The transform of such functions can be found directly from products of familiar one-dimensional transforms, as shown in Table 6.1.

6.2 OPTICS

The system optics perform a variety of tasks, as outlined in Chapter 2. Fundamental to all the types of systems considered here are the objective optics. The objective optics receive the incoming radiation and form a real image of a distant scene. In the EO systems considered here this real image usually falls directly on a sensor. Sometimes the basic objective optics are preceded by replaceable afocal (or tele-

Table 6.1

Transform Pairs

Function	Transform
$\exp[-\pi(x^2 + y^2)]$	$\exp[-\pi(\nu_x^2 + \nu_y^2)]$
$\text{rect}(x)\,\text{rect}(y)$	$\text{sinc}(\nu_x)\,\text{sinc}(\nu_y)$
$\Lambda(x)\,\Lambda(y)$	$\text{sinc}^2(\nu_x)\,\text{sinc}^2(\nu_y)$
$\delta(x, y)$	1
$\exp[j\pi(x + y)]$	$\delta\left(\nu_x - \dfrac{1}{2}, \nu_y - \dfrac{1}{2}\right)$
$\text{sgn}(x)\,\text{sgn}(y)$	$\dfrac{1}{j\pi\nu_x}\dfrac{1}{j\pi\nu_y}$
$\text{comb}(x)\,\text{comb}(y)$	$\text{comb}(\nu_x)\,\text{comb}(\nu_y)$

scopic) optics to adjust the system magnification and field of view; this is often the case for FLIR front-end optics.

6.2.1 Perfect Imaging Systems

We first confine our attention to an idealization of optical systems called *perfect imaging systems*. These are defined by their adherence to the following rules:

1. All rays originating at one object point reconverge to one image point after passing through the system.
2. All the object points lying on one plane normal to the optical axis are imaged onto one plane normal to the axis.
3. The image is geometrically similar to the object.

As in most aspects of engineering, no real optical system is exactly perfect in this sense. However, well-designed systems approach this ideal very closely, and the perfect imaging system is a good starting point for learning optical system design principles.

6.2.1.1 Magnification

Rule 3 for perfect imaging systems means that the image looks like the object: it is a replica, but generally of a different size. Magnification for an imaging system is defined as a linear dimension of the image, d_I, divided by the corresponding linear dimension of the object, d_O:

$$m \equiv d_I/d_O \tag{6.35}$$

6.2.1.2 Effective Focal Length

For any perfect imaging system the most important system descriptor is *effective focal length*, often written EFL. It can be defined by considering the system's image of a distant object that subtends in one dimension, the small angle, δ, at the system. Then if d_I is the image size in the same dimension, the EFL is given by

$$f \equiv d_I/\delta \qquad (6.36)$$

For this to hold, the object should be many times farther away than the EFL value, and the angle it subtends should be less than or equal to .1 rad. Also, because the object is far away, we do not have to be very specific about the point in the imaging system from which we measure the angle.

The importance of EFL stems from it being the one system variable the designer has to control image size. There is a direct relationship that we can express by substituting the following for the δ in (6.36):

$$d_I = \frac{d_o}{R}f \qquad (6.37)$$

Also (6.37) can be combined with (6.35) for a distant object to give

$$m = f/R \qquad (6.38)$$

The definition of EFL given is quite general and does not depend on the type of imaging system. EFL is not necessarily the distance from the back optical surface to the image plane for a distant object. This image plane for a distant object is known as the *focal plane*, and the distance from the back physical surface to the focal plane is called the *back focal length* (BFL). Although BFL is convenient to know for mechanical reasons, it has no inherent connection to the image size, as does EFL.

Any perfect imaging lens is reversible: it may be turned around and used the opposite way, in which case it still forms the same size image and still has the same EFL. This result follows from the fact that light (or IR) rays themselves are reversible. Therefore we may think of the imaging lens as having two focal planes, one on either side. The focal plane toward the object is called the *front focal plane* and that toward the image (at which the image is formed if the object is distant) is called the *back focal plane*. The distance from the first surface of the system to the front focal plane is called the *front focal length* (FFL), and it is not necessarily equal to either EFL or BFL.

Although the EFL is the same no matter which way the lens is used, the same does not generally hold true for other descriptive parameters of the system, like pupils and aberrations (both to be discussed later). Therefore a given lens system is usually used in only one direction. Furthermore, because mirrors reflect from only one surface, they are not reversible in the same manner as lenses.

6.2.1.3 Principal Planes

In addition to the focal planes, two other planes associated with a perfect imaging system are quite useful in its description: the principal or unit planes. If we start at the front focal plane and move a distance equal to the EFL toward the system and parallel to the optical axis, we arrive at the primary principal plane. Or, starting at the back focal plane and moving the same distance (EFL) in the same manner toward the system, we arrive at the secondary principal plane. In other words, a perfect imaging system is characterized by four planes perpendicular to the optical axis: the front focal plane and the primary principal plane, the secondary principal plane and the back focal plane, each pair separated by the EFL. The spacing between the two principal planes depends on the design of the system. The principal points (primary and secondary) are defined as the intersections of the principal planes with the optical axis. Figure 6.6 illustrates these concepts.

A very simple imaging system is a single thin lens. For a thin lens the spacing between the principal planes is 0, so it can really be characterized by its focal planes (or EFL) and a single principal plane at the center of the lens. It is important to

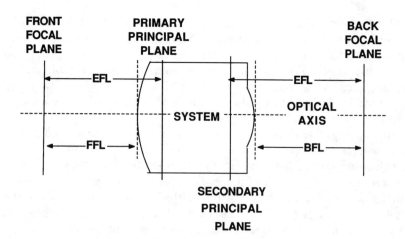

Figure 6.6 Perfect imaging system parameters.

realize, however, that, no matter how complicated the imaging system, if it approximates a perfect imaging system only two principal planes are needed to describe it.

6.2.1.4   Ray Tracing

It is very useful for a system designer to be able to trace the path of light rays through the optical system. This procedure is known as *ray tracing*. For system design purposes it is not necessary to know the details of the imaging system components, but instead we may replace the system by its principal planes and focal planes.

Consider a bundle of light rays entering the system from a point in the scene, as shown in Figure 6.7. We are assuming the scene is so far away that the rays from one object point that enter the system are essentially parallel to each other as shown. Because the image of this point is formed in the back focal plane of the system, all these rays converge to a point there. The rule for transport of the rays between principal planes is simply that each ray is translated parallel to the optical axis in that region, no matter what its direction was before the first principal plane. Then the central ray (through the primary principal point) in the bundle is undeviated in direction (although displaced by the transport between the principal planes) from its original path. Where this ray crosses the back focal plane fixes the image point to which all the other rays must converge.

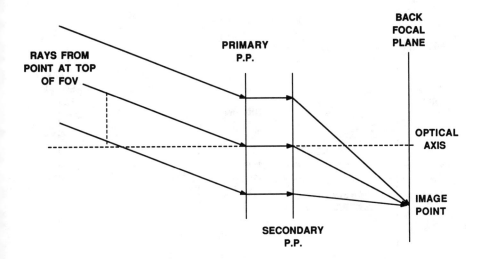

Figure 6.7 Tracing rays through a perfect imaging system.

Because of the parallel transport of rays between the principal planes, any two rays that come together at the primary principal plane must still be together at the secondary one. Therefore the two principal planes represent exact images of one another with unity magnification. This is the reason for the name *unit planes*. Figure 6.8 illustrates this relation.

The concept of a parallel central ray can be used to trace the path of any general ray through the system. Once the general ray in question is drawn to the first unit plane, draw an imaginary parallel ray to the primary principal point, as in Figure 6.9. Continue both rays parallel to the optical axis between the unit planes. Now the imaginary ray can be extended from the secondary principal plane

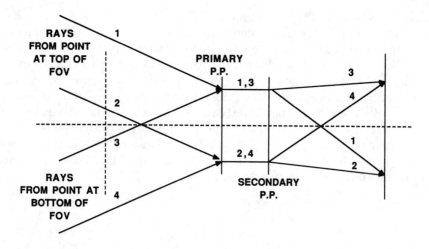

Figure 6.8 Unit planes of a perfect imaging system.

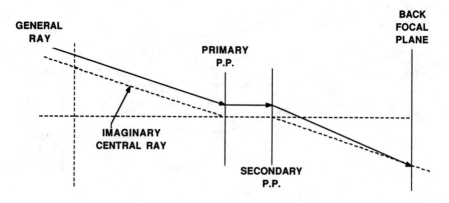

Figure 6.9 Tracing a general ray through a perfect imaging system.

to the back focal plane parallel to its original path to find the intersection with the focal plane. The intersection point so found becomes the straight-line destination of the real ray extended from the secondary principal plane.

Any incoming ray parallel to the axis becomes very easy to trace according to these rules. Such a ray will always continue straight through to the secondary principal plane, from which it proceeds to the back focal point, the point where the back focal plane intersects the optical axis.

6.2.1.5 Stops and Pupils

A complete description of even a perfect imaging system includes more than knowledge of the optical axis, principal planes, and focal planes. Somewhere in the imaging system is an aperture that physically limits the size of a parallel bundle of rays that the system accepts. This opening is called the *aperture stop*. Often, but not always, the aperture stop is the clear opening of the first surface. Sometimes an iris diaphragm in front of or behind the first surface serves as an aperture stop. Figure 6.10 shows some of the possibilities.

The image of the aperture stop in all the system elements preceding it is defined as the entrance pupil of the system. The entrance pupil is the effective

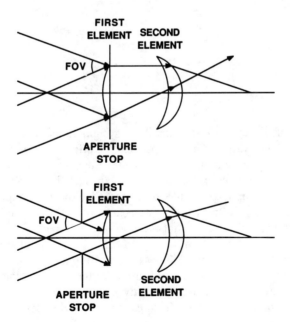

Figure 6.10 Possible aperture stop positions.

aperture of the system, as seen by the incoming bundle of rays. If the aperture stop is right at the first surface of the system then it is identical with the entrance pupil. Figure 6.11 illustrates a situation where this is not the case. Now the chief ray can be properly defined as the ray in a parallel that which passes through the center of the entrance pupil.

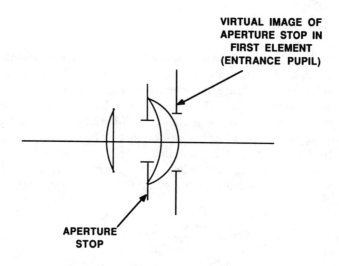

Figure 6.11 Entrance pupil as an image of an aperture stop.

The image of the aperture stop in all the system elements behind it is defined as the exit pupil of the system. The exit pupil is the effective aperture of the system as seen from image space. Figure 6.12 illustrates the case where the aperture stop is the first surface: in this case the principal planes of the whole system may be used to find the exit pupil. It should be noted that the exit pupil is always the image of entrance pupil in the whole system, and therefore if the latter is known the former may be found by the usual method of ray tracing.

Sometimes in complex systems images of the entrance pupil are formed within the system before the final exit pupil. These we may think of as intermediate pupils. The positions of these intermediate pupils are excellent for the placement of filters or any other elements we wish to uniformly affect the whole field of view. We know the entrance pupil has the rays from each point in the scene spread uniformly across it, and therefore, because any intermediate pupil is an image of the entrance pupil, it will share the same property.

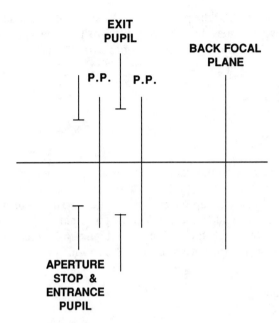

Figure 6.12 Exit pupil as an image of an aperture stop.

6.2.1.6 Conjugate Relations

Finding the exit pupil from the entrance pupil and principal planes and focal planes of the system is an example of finding the image of a nearby object rather than a distant one. Although ray tracing will work, it is convenient to have a formula for finding the position of the image. Fortunately there is a simple equation relating object position, image position, and EFL:

$$1/p + 1/q = 1/f \tag{6.39}$$

where

p = object distance (object to primary principal plane)
q = image distance (secondary principal plane to image)
f = EFL.

Equation (6.39) shows symmetry in q and p, indicating that the image and object could be interchanged (a reflection of the reversibility of light rays). Also (6.39) includes the special case of a very distant object: $p = \infty \Rightarrow q = f$. This equation may be used to find the position of the exit pupil when that of the entrance pupil is known. More generally it may be used to find the position of any image when the object position is known. Furthermore it may be used to find magnification because it is also true that

$$q/p = d_i/d_o \equiv m \qquad (6.40)$$

6.2.1.7 Field of View

For people who are new to optical systems, there is often confusion between the aperture and the field of view (FOV) of a system. The FOV refers to the angle over which ray bundles are accepted from the scene, and it is determined by another stop within the system, called the *field stop*. The field stop is located within an image plane (often the back focal plane), as Figure 6.13 illustrates. FOV is not related to the size of the aperture stop or the entrance pupil. We may write

$$\tan(FOV/2) = \frac{d_f}{2f} \qquad (6.41)$$

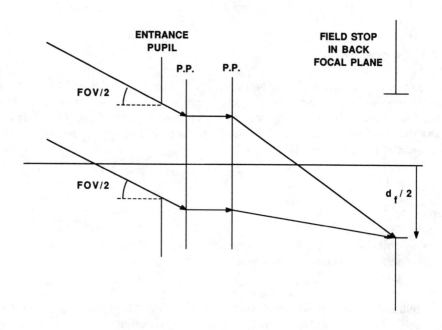

Figure 6.13 Field stop and field of view.

where d_f if the linear dimension of field stop. For a circular field stop, d_f would be the diameter, and there is only one value of FOV. For a rectangular field stop, there would be both a horizontal and vertical FOV, corresponding to the two values of d_f. Often FOV is a small angle, so

$$\text{FOV} \approx d_f/f \tag{6.42}$$

In scanning systems, an image is scanned or dissected in some manner. In this case the scanned area is the field stop, and FOV is calculated accordingly. However, there is another field of view of interest, which is called the *instantaneous field of view* (IFOV). This is determined by the size of a single resolution element (single detector, cathode ray beam, *et cetera*). In this case, (6.42) is almost always a very good approximation.

6.2.1.8 Vignetting

The design defect known as *vignetting* occurs when there is a mismatch between the aperture stop and the field stop, and it leads to an image that is shaded toward its outer edges. Figure 6.14 shows how this happens: there is effectively a different size aperture stop for the edges and the center of the field of view. To eliminate vignetting one may increase the size of the aperture stop for the off-axis rays or decrease the size of the field stop. However, neither of these options may be satisfactory, because the one may imply unacceptably large components whereas the other may imply an unacceptably small FOV.

Another approach often employed uses a field lens at, or near the position of, an internal image plane. The field lens can bend the ray bundles from the outer edge of the FOV so that the whole bundle passes through the obstructing component, without significantly affecting the EFL of the system.

6.2.1.9 Image Radiometry

In Chapter 5 we arrived at an expression for the irradiance (or illuminance) at the entrance pupil to the system, which is accurate as long as the area of source viewed, A_s, is small compared to the range, R, squared. This condition is certainly always satisfied if the system FOV is small and may be satisfied in any case for a small object within the FOV. The expression is:

$$E = L(R)A_s/R^2 \tag{6.43}$$

where $L(R)$ is the source radiance at range R as altered by the atmosphere. We

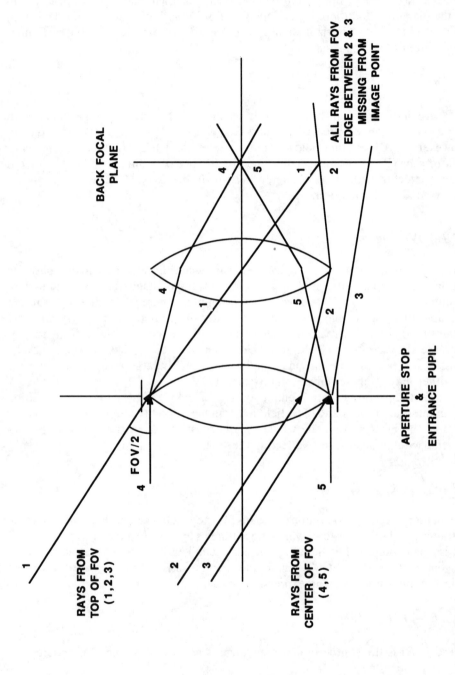

Figure 6.14 Vignetting.

may now carry this radiation through the system to the image. We assume a distant object so that the image is in the back focal plane.

In the first place an optical system never transmits every bit of received radiation, but always absorbs or reflects some. Therefore the optical system is characterized by a transmittance τ_o. The flux passed through the system is then

$$\phi = E \cdot \tau_o \cdot A_E$$

where A_E is the area of the entrance pupil. The irradiance in the image is just this flux divided by the area of the image, A_I.

$$E_I = [\tau_o A_E L(R)/R^2](A_s/A_I) \tag{6.44}$$

The area of the source and the area of the image are grouped together in (6.44) because they correspond to each other: the image we mean here is the image of the source, whatever that is considered to be. If the source is considered to be the whole FOV then A_I is the area of the image of the whole FOV. But, if the source is considered to be some object within the FOV, then A_I is just the area of that object's image. This means that there is a constant relationship between the two areas:

$$A_s/A_I = 1/m^2 = R^2/f^2 \tag{6.45}$$

Here it has been assumed that the scene viewed is distant so that (6.38) may be used for system magnification. When (6.45) is used with (6.44) and a circular entrance pupil is assumed, we get

$$E_I = \frac{\pi}{4} \tau_o d_E^2 L(R)/f^2 \tag{6.46}$$

where d_E is the entrance pupil diameter.

Equation (6.46) prompts the definition of a quantity called the *system F-number*. This is defined as the EFL divided by entrance pupil diameter:

$$F \equiv f/d_E \tag{6.47}$$

Then irradiance in the image is simply expressed by

$$E_I = \frac{\pi}{4} \tau_o L(R)/F^2 \tag{6.48}$$

Additional compactness may be achieved by defining system T-number as the F-number divided by the square root of system transmittance. Then

$$T \equiv F/\tau_o^{1/2} \tag{6.49}$$

$$E_I = \frac{\pi}{4} L(R)/T^2 \tag{6.50}$$

We can see from these equations that there is a strong dependence of image irradiance on the system F-number. The smaller is the F-number, the better it is for this purpose: cutting the F-number in half actually will increase irradiance in the image by a factor of 4. Because the sensors need a higher image irradiance in general to give larger signal-to-noise ratios in their output, we can see that the F-number is a very important system parameter.

6.2.2 Diffraction

Our treatment of the perfect imaging system used the geometrical optics approximation: radiation is characterized only by rays that are straight lines showing the direction of motion. However, in reality, electromagnetic radiation consists of waves, and any detailed treatment of imaging systems must eventually take account of this wave nature. In doing so we find that the wave nature of electromagnetic radiation does not allow strict adherence to rule 1 for perfect imaging systems, no matter how perfect the design of the system. Instead wave interference always spreads the radiation from a single object point into a blur circle in the image plane that subtends a half-angle at the exit pupil (assumed circular) of

$$\theta_d = 1.22\lambda/d_E \tag{6.51}$$

where d_E is the entrance pupil diameter.

To be more precise, the waves from an object point form an interference pattern in the image plane that is composed of this blur circle surrounded by a set of concentric rings, but most of the power is in the central spot. This spreading of radiation past the boundaries predicted by geometrical optics, due to the finite aperture of the system, is known as *diffraction*. The radius of the diffraction blur spot would be given, assuming a distant source, approximately by

$$r_b \approx 1.22\lambda f/d_E = 1.22\lambda F \tag{6.52}$$

6.2.3 Aberrations

The divergence of a real imaging system from the ideal within the geometrical optics approximation is expressed by a series of aberrations. There are five mono-chromatic aberrations in addition to a chromatic aberration, which occurs only when there is a band of wavelengths in the radiation. The five monochromatic aberrations are as follows.

1. Spherical aberration occurs because, for spherical surfaces on the optical components, different zones of the reflecting or refracting surface produce slightly different focal points along the optical axis. Outer zones produce a longer focal length.
2. Coma occurs for off-axis points because different zones of the surface produce slightly different magnifications and slightly different image positions laterally (off-axis).
3. Astigmatism results for off-axis points because the focal length in the tan-gential plane (containing the optical axis and tilted in the off-axis direction) is slightly different than that in the sagittal plane (containing the optical axis and perpendicular to the tangential plane).
4. Field curvature occurs because a plane normal to the optical axis is not imaged into another normal to the axis, as for perfect imaging systems, but rather into a curved surface.
5. Distortion is due to the fact that magnification can vary somewhat with distance of the image from the optical axis.

The chromatic aberration arises from the fact that dispersion is an unavoidable process within refracting materials. Dispersion is the dependence of the refractive index on the frequency of the radiation: different frequencies will be refracted by different amounts. The result is that a lens will also act like a prism, having a shorter focal length for higher frequencies (shorter wavelengths). It is the only other on-axis aberration besides the spherical.

The job of the optical designer, rather than the system designer or analyst, is to wrestle with the details of the imaging system to minimize these aberrations within the other system constraints. Instead, the system analyst needs a general way to specify the imperfect, real-life imaging system, preferably a way that can be related directly to overall system performance. This can be done with the modulation transfer function.

6.2.4 Optical Transfer Function

An imaging system can be characterized by a two-dimensional optical transfer function (assuming incoherent imaging), the modulus of which is the modulation transfer function of the optics. The modulation transfer function essentially gives the modulation reduction of the imaging system *versus* spatial frequency when a sinusoidal radiance pattern is imaged. This is true because the imaging system, at least approximately, linearly combines contributions from different points in the object plane to produce irradiance at a point in the image plane. In fact for our idealization of a perfect imaging system the spread function is just a Dirac delta function: only one point in the object plane contributes to a point in the image plane. Therefore the modulation transfer function is unity for all spatial frequencies, meaning no frequency would suffer a modulation reduction, and we would indeed have a "perfect" imaging system.

6.2.4.1 Diffraction-Limited Imaging

Because diffraction mixes the radiation from an area of the object plane at one image point (or spreads the radiation from one object point over a small area of the image) the spread function for any real imaging system, even without aberrations, must have some nonzero width. Therefore a diffraction-limited imaging system has an MTF that falls off with increasing spatial frequency.

For the MTF of a diffraction-limited system it will be useful to define the normalized spatial frequency, η, as the ratio of spatial frequency to the cutoff spatial frequency:

$$\eta \equiv v_s/v_c \tag{6.53}$$

The cutoff frequency may then be expressed in cycles/length or cycles/angle (usually c/mm or c/mr) depending on the desired units for v_s:

$$v_c = \frac{1}{\lambda f} = 1.22/r_b \quad \text{(c/mm)} \tag{6.54}$$

$$v_c = d_E/\lambda = 1.22/\theta_d \quad \text{(c/mr)} \tag{6.55}$$

Then the diffraction-limited MTF is given by

$$\text{MTF}_{OD} = \frac{2}{\pi} (\cos^{-1}\eta - \eta\sqrt{1 - \eta^2}), \quad \eta < 1$$

$$= 0, \quad \eta \geq 1 \tag{6.56}$$

This function is plotted in Figure 6.15. We can see that it is very nearly a straight

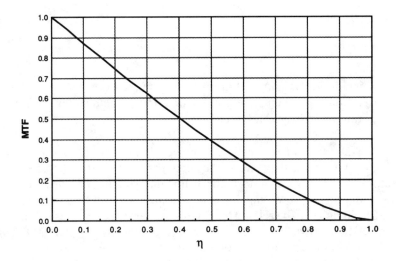

Figure 6.15 Diffraction-limited optics MTF.

line, especially for lower values of η. In fact there is a very good straight-line approximation for $\eta \leq .6$:

$$\text{MTF}_{OD} \approx 1 - 1.218\,\eta \tag{6.57}$$

6.2.4.2 Imaging with Aberrations

When aberrations are present in the imaging system, the MTF is degraded from that of the diffraction-limited case. In fact the MTF with aberrations will be less at all nonzero frequencies. Although the amount of each type of aberration can be related to the resulting MTF [1], the system analyst is usually not interested in such details. It suffices to have a measured MTF curve.

Sometimes it is convenient to have a single-value figure of merit or performance measure instead of a curve, because it can be difficult to compare curves. For example, a variation in transmittance across the entrance or exit pupil can increase the MTF over the diffraction-limited case at certain frequencies, but only at the expense of degradation at other frequencies. Is this better than the diffraction-limited case? Or how do we compare two MTF curves of different shape for different aberration combinations if they cross each other a number of times?

One of the most widely used imaging-system single-value performance measures is called the *Strehl ratio* or *Strehl definition*. It is defined by a ratio of image irradiances (or illuminances):

$$\mathcal{D} \equiv E_I/E_{ID} \tag{6.58}$$

where

E_I = irradiance at center of point source image from system
E_{ID} = irradiance at center of point source image from system without aberrations (diffraction limited).

Because aberrations tend to spread the power from a point source beyond the spread due to diffraction, the peak at the center of the pattern is lowered and $\mathcal{D} \leq$ 1. Therefore $\mathcal{D}$ can serve as a normalized imaging system performance measure, with a value of unity representing diffraction-limited, aberration-free performance.

The Strehl ratio can be related to imaging system MTF. Because of the Fourier transform relation between system point spread function and system MTF, we can see that the Strehl ratio equals the volume under the two-dimensional system MTF curve divided by the volume under the diffraction-limited MTF curve:

$$\mathcal{D} = \int\int_0^\infty \text{MTF}_O \, d\nu_x d\nu_y \Big/ \int\int_0^\infty \text{MTF}_{OD} \, d\nu_x d\nu_y \tag{6.59}$$

The value $\mathcal{D} \geq .8$ is widely accepted [2] as a mark of "good" optics.

Although nothing is better than having a measured MTF curve for the optics, if one assumes the MTF is a smooth curve that can be approximated by a second-order polynomial, then the Strehl ratio value can be used, along with (6.59), to construct such a curve. We assume circular symmetry for the optics, and therefore also for the MTF:

$$\text{MTF}_O(\eta) = A\eta^2 + B\eta + C \tag{6.60}$$

with boundary conditions

$$\text{MTF}_O(0) = C = 1 \tag{6.61}$$

$$\text{MTF}_O(1) = A + B + 1 = 0$$
$$B = -(1 + A) \tag{6.62}$$

The integral in the numerator of (6.59), using cylindrical coordinates, becomes

$$2\pi \int_0^1 [A\eta^2 - (1 + A)\eta + 1]\eta \, d\eta = \frac{\pi}{3}\left(1 - \frac{1}{2}A\right) \tag{6.63}$$

Then performing the integral in the denominator of (6.59) in the same manner gives

$$2\pi \int_0^1 \frac{2}{\pi} (\cos^{-1}\eta - \eta\sqrt{1 - \eta^2})\eta\, d\eta = \frac{\pi}{4} \tag{6.64}$$

Finally combining (6.63) and (6.64) with (6.59) produces the result

$$A = 2 - 1.5\mathcal{D} \tag{6.65}$$

We conclude that the second-order polynomial approximation to the MTF for our circularly symmetric optics, which gives the correct Strehl ratio, is

$$\mathrm{MTF}_O(\eta) \approx (2 - 1.5\mathcal{D})\eta^2 + (1.5\mathcal{D} - 3)\eta + 1 \tag{6.66}$$

6.2.5 Afocal or Telescopic Systems

The telescopic system, also known as an *afocal system*, does not quite fit the category of perfect imaging system, even when diffraction and aberrations are ignored. The reason for this is because it does not conform to rule 1 for perfect imaging systems. Instead, all rays originating at a distant object point are made parallel by an afocal system; that is, they enter the system parallel due to the long range and exit the system still parallel. In this case the principal planes of the system cannot be unambiguously defined and EFL $= \pm\infty$.

Figure 6.16 shows a ray diagram for a simple type of telescopic system, with single thin lenses for the objective and eyepiece. We say there is a final virtual image produced at infinity, because the exiting parallel rays can be interpreted as coming from a very distant image. As shown in the diagram, the final image is inverted, but it may be turned upright by an additional erecting lens or the proper sequence of reflections between the objective and the eyepiece.

When the system is used as a telescopic sight for direct viewing, the eye should be placed at the position of the exit pupil. The distance from the last physical surface to the exit pupil is known as the eye relief. In this case the exit pupil should be no larger than the eye's pupil, otherwise some of the light collected by the system entrance pupil will be wasted.

When the system serves as the front end to another imaging system the exit pupil of the former should be coincident with the entrance pupil of the latter. These pupils should also be matched in size, so that no collected light is lost to the imaging system and none of its aperture is wasted.

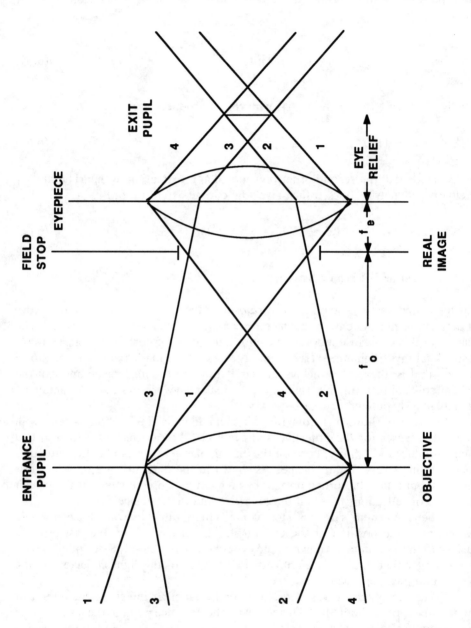

Figure 6.16 Ray diagram for afocal or telescopic optics.

For an afocal system the previous definition of magnification, (6.35), is not very useful: because the object and final virtual image are both very distant, their linear size cannot be measured directly. However, their angular size can; and because a linear dimension is proportional to angle subtended for small angles, we define angular magnification:

$$m \equiv \delta_I/\delta_O \tag{6.67}$$

where

δ_I = angle subtended by distant image
δ_O = angle subtended by distant object.

We can see from the ray diagram that

$$m \approx f_o/f_e \tag{6.68}$$

where

f_o = objective EFL
f_e = eyepiece EFL.

Another very useful relation for an afocal system is

$$m = d_E/d_e \tag{6.69}$$

where

d_E = entrance pupil diameter
d_e = exit pupil diameter.

In the case of a telescopic sight this magnification specifies how much bigger things look through the sight than with the naked eye. If the afocal system is the front end of an imaging system, then this magnification just multiplies the image size that would pertain without the afocal system in front.

6.3   ELECTRONICS

In the previous section we addressed the optical portion of the electro-optical system. In this section we complete the transfer from a photon image to an electronic image. For TV systems this is reasonably straightforward, in that the scene is directly imaged onto the detector, which converts photon energy into electrical energy. This in turn is amplified and processed and forwarded to the display. With IR systems we need to encompass the analysis of the three types of scanning mechanisms usually encountered—serial, parallel, and staring—as well as the detector and processing.

The electronics is addressed in terms of its impact on the displayed image quality. Throughout this electronics section we will continue to address image quality in terms of the overall impact of the electronics in reducing the MTF. By its nature, the inclusion of electronics will also introduce such measures as dynamic range, sensitivities, limits and thresholds, and the signal-to-noise ratio. In this section we will discuss the system analysis and impact of scanners, detectors, and signal processing.

6.3.1 FLIR Scanners

In Chapter 2, various types of FLIRs were described. Of the three types (staring, parallel, and serial scanned), the latter two types both require some mechanism for scanning either an array of detectors or a point detector over the total field of view. If the array of detectors is a column equivalent to the vertical field of view, then the scanning mechanism is a one-dimensional scanner. Two-dimensional scanners are required for point detector or arrays that do not fill the field of view of the FLIR. All serial scanned FLIRs have two-dimensional scanners. Parallel scanned devices essentially scan in one dimension per frame but often have a "nodder" in the other dimension to produce the interlaced scan.

FLIRs historically were produced as scanning devices because of the inherent difficulty of making large arrays of detector material with uniformly high detectivity and reasonable yield. Larger arrays also produce problems in getting the individual detector voltages off the array in some organized manner in order to provide a real-time video signal. Today we look to lay the array of IR-sensitive detector material (such as HgCdTe) onto a silicon back plane configured as a *charge-coupled device* (CCD) and clock the detector voltage out through the CCD. The result is a focal plane array. Manufacture-yield problems to date have limited the size of focal plane arrays. Although staring arrays of reasonable resolution are starting to occur, by far the majority of fielded FLIRs are scanned devices. Staring arrays made of PtSi are available today, albeit in the 3–5 μm band, and many of the production problems associated with large (256 × 256 or greater) HgCdTe arrays are being solved. The future clearly belongs to focal plane arrays, in particular staring focal plane arrays. Although the future belongs to staring arrays, the past and present belong to scanning systems.

6.3.1.1 Type of Scanners

There are two basic types of scanners, parallel beam and converging beam scanners, as shown in Figure 6.17. The parallel beam scanner consists of an optical angle changing device such as a moving mirror placed in front of the final image forming lens. For the converging beam scanner the optical angle changing device is placed between the final image and the lens.

6.3.1.2 Scanning Techniques

Many different scanning techniques are well referenced in the 1978 version of *The Infrared Handbook* [3]. The important parameters, when addressing how to cause an instantaneous field of view to scan or sample a total field of view, are scan rate, scan rate constancy, scan efficiency, optical efficiency, and vignetting.

The more commonly encountered mechanisms for scanning are the oscillating plane mirrors and the rotating polygon scanners. In the serial scan devices both mechanisms are sometimes mixed, with the horizontal axis being scanned by using a rotating polygon and the vertical axis by utilizing an oscillating plane mirror.

It is not the intent of this chapter to cover the detailed description of various scanning mechanisms. The subject is well covered in [3]. We have included one example in the following text so that the reader has some understanding of the scanning operation. We have chosen the oscillating plane mirror as our example; however, what is important to this chapter is the inclusion of such parameters as scan efficiency, MTF, and so on in the analysis of the FLIR performance. When the reader meets other scanners we expect he or she will be able to draw a parallel to the oscillating plane mirror.

The principle of the oscillating plane mirror is as shown in Figure 6.18. It can be used either as a parallel beam or a convergent beam scanner. The mirror oscillates periodically between two stops producing a ray angular deviation of twice the mirror angle change.

Scanners suffer from intrinsic errors, such as a loss in MTF at the edges of a scan, shading, and vignetting. The first is caused by the change in path length at various scan angles. All of these errors are well understood and, in a good FLIR, are already corrected or compensated by the FLIR designer. The system analyst of today is unlikely to have to perform an overall MTF analysis at various scan angles.

6.3.1.3 Scan Patterns

In general, six different types of scan patterns are associated with FLIRs, as shown in Table 6.2. All of these are interesting scan patterns, but the one that predom-

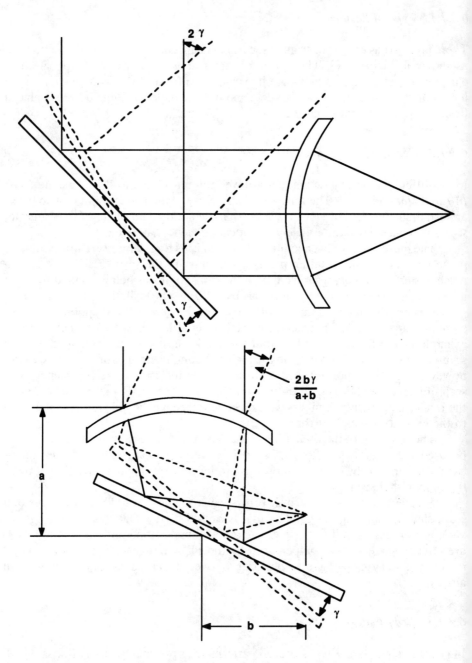

Figure 6.17 Parallel beam and converging beam scanners.

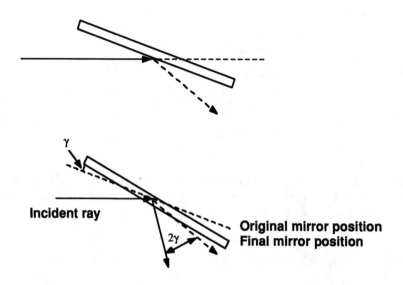

Figure 6.18 Oscillating plane mirror scanner.

inates in FLIRs is the raster scan, either sequential or interlaced. Figure 6.19 shows a typical, single-line contiguous two-directional scan. The cross-hatching is meant to show that each successive line advances by an average of one-half of the line width at the scan line edges. The scan has, therefore, a 100% overlap or, as we shall see later, a scan efficiency of 50%.

6.3.1.4 Scanning Parameters and Signal-to-Noise Ratio

The *signal-to-noise ratio* (SNR) of a scanning infrared system is given in the simplified form (see eq. (6.93) for a more rigorous formulation) by

$$\text{SNR} = D^* \phi_d A_d^{-1/2} \Delta\nu^{-1/2} \tag{6.70}$$

where

D^* = detectivity
ϕ_d = power or flux on the detector
A_d = effective area of the detector
$\Delta\nu$ = noise bandwidth.

The noise bandwidth is inversely proportional to the dwell time on a single

Table 6.2
Scan Patterns

Raster scans
Transverse line scans
Stationary circular patterns
Translated circle (or Palmer) scans
Rotating prism scans
Cycloidal patterns

resolution element. If the scanning velocity is constant over the total field and only the field is covered, then the dwell time, t_d, for a frame is given by $t_d = t_f/N$, where N is the number of resolution elements and t_f is the frame time.

6.3.1.5 Dead Time Relationships

If there is some dead time t_f' during the frame, then the dwell time is $t_d = t_f - t_f'$ and the scan efficiency is given by

$$\eta_s = \frac{t_f - t_f'}{t_f} \tag{6.71}$$

6.3.1.6 Variable Scan Velocity

If the scan velocity is not constant, then the noise bandwidth is determined by the maximum scan velocity, and the scan efficiency is degraded by the relationship

$$\eta = \bar{v}/v_m \tag{6.72}$$

where

v_m = maximum scan velocity
$\bar{v}$ = average scan velocity.

6.3.1.7 Overlap (or Overscan) Relationships

If the scan lines overlap, the scanning is not 100% efficient. If the overscan ratio is designated r_o, then the frame time for a frame with N_1 lines is given by

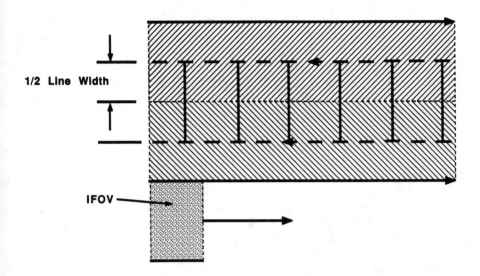

1/2 Line Width

IFOV

Figure 6.19 Typical raster scan.

$$t_f = t_1 N_1 (1 + r_o) \tag{6.73}$$

where t_1 is the time for one line.

If there are N_r resolution elements (i.e., IFOV) in a line then the dwell time for a constant scan velocity is given by

$$t_d = (t_1/N_r)(1 + r_o)^{-1} \tag{6.74}$$

The scan efficiency is therefore

$$\eta_s = (1 + r_o)^{-1} \tag{6.75}$$

Although overlap loses SNR because of loss of information bandwidth B, it also compensates somewhat according to the general square root relationship.

6.3.1.8 Shading Effects

In certain types of suboptimal FLIR designs the displayed scene has superimposed on it a broad, slowly varying spurious signal. This image defect is called *shading*, either signal dependent or signal independent, after a similar but unrelated effect in television camera tubes. Shading should not be present in a well-designed FLIR, and so we will not dwell at length on the subject. The reader however should be aware of the potential presence of shading in the image and the need to minimize its impact. In itself, such shading may not be too objectionable if it is limited to a few percent of the maximum displayed scene luminance. However, if the FLIR is to be used to provide inputs to an automatic target motion tracker or to some automatic target classification device, shading must be minimized. When optical design alone cannot eliminate shading, electronic compensation and optical baffling can be employed.

6.3.1.9 Summary of Scanning Mechanisms and Techniques

Luckily a system designer rarely has the luxury of choosing the scanning mechanism. This dubious responsibility falls to the FLIR designer. It behooves the FLIR system designer to understand the principle of the scanning mechanism within the FLIR and its impact not only on SNR but also on image quality. The system designer is responsible for ensuring the right FLIR is used for the right application. The human eye is reasonably forgiving when it comes to shading or vignetting, but an automatic target tracker is not. The more background a system designer has, the less likely he or she is to fall into one of the many pitfalls. FLIR systems initially chosen for their human-related detection performance cannot automatically be used for automatic target trackers without a great deal of careful investigation of the image artifacts caused by the scanning mechanism.

6.3.2 Detectors

The heart of any sensor system is the detector. The system performance is ultimately determined by the performance of the detecting transducer, that element which converts the incoming radiant energy into electrical signals. Such devices are therefore radiation transducers. There are many types of transduction devices; for electro-optical systems there are principally two, the photo emissive and the photo conductive. For thermal devices there are principally two classes, thermal detectors and photon detectors. These two classes contain the subclasses shown in Table 6.3.

Table 6.3
Methods of Transduction in IR Region

Thermal Detectors	Photon Detectors
Bolometric	Photovoltaic
Thermovoltaic	Photoconductive
Thermopneumatic	Photoelectromagnetic
Pyroelectric	Photoemissive

Usually the device that best fits the application is chosen. It is interesting to note that the majority of TV and FLIR cameras we meet today use photoconductive materials. We shall therefore concentrate on solid-state photoconductive devices and materials for both the visible band, the 3–5 μm band, and the 8–14 μm band.

6.3.2.1   Optical Detectors

In selecting and evaluating optical detectors we look for a common methodology and a common figure of merit for comparing one sensor against another. The evaluation has to include ways of quantifying such parameters as the contribution of the detector to the overall system measures of performance; for example, MTF, SNR, and dynamic range. For optical detectors it is important that all evaluations be measured spectrally. An optical detector is a transducer that converts incident radiant flux in the optical band, generally, to a single (electrical) voltage output. The detector can be thought of in terms of a transfer function designated responsivity ($\mathcal{R}$) that is the response of the output current (or voltage) to the input flux in watts or lumens. As the response of a detector is wavelength dependent, the device response is often more meaningfully expressed as a spectral responsivity ($\mathcal{R}(\lambda)$).

There are many acceptable ways of expressing the input flux. It is usually expressed as radiant flux over a given band of wavelengths, although in some references the number of quanta per second, luminous flux, and flux density (flux per unit area in the plane of the device) are also used. The number of quanta due to a spectral radiant flux is given by

$$N = \frac{\lambda \phi_\lambda \, d\lambda}{hc} \tag{6.76}$$

where $\phi_\lambda \, d\lambda$ represents the radiant flux per unit wavelength increment in watts, and hc/λ is the energy of a single quantum (h being Planck's constant). The responsivity is given by

$$\mathcal{R}(\lambda) = \frac{I_s}{\phi_\lambda \, d\lambda} \tag{6.77}$$

The signal current out of the device represents the output due to the total incident luminous flux integrated over the detector response; therefore,

$$I_s = \int_{\lambda_1}^{\lambda_2} \mathcal{R}_\lambda \phi_\lambda \, d\lambda \tag{6.78}$$

We often see a detector evaluated in terms of quantum efficiency. *Quantum efficiency* $\eta(\lambda)$ refers to the ratio of photoelectrons emitted (i.e., the electron hole pairs generated) to the absorbed quanta. It is a meaningful figure when expressed for the prime photosensor and is less than unity. When, as is in certain cases of cascaded sensors such as image intensified cameras, there is an intrinsic stage of light amplification, this figure of merit in the strict definition exceeds unity and loses its value as a meaningful measure. It is usually expressed as a spectral value; that is, defined at a given wavelength:

$$\eta(\lambda) = \frac{\text{number of electrons per second}}{\text{number of incident quanta at wavelength } \lambda} \tag{6.79}$$

The number of photoelectrons per second is given by

$$I_s/e = \mathscr{R}(\lambda)\,\phi_\lambda\,d\lambda/e \tag{6.80}$$

The number of incident photons is

$$N = \frac{\lambda\phi_\lambda\,d\lambda}{hc} \tag{6.81}$$

hence

$$\eta(\lambda) = \frac{\mathscr{R}(\lambda)hc}{e\lambda} \tag{6.82}$$

Typical quantum efficiencies and spectral response curves for typical photodetectors in the visible range are given in Figure 6.20.

A photodetector has a current that flows in the absence of incident radiation. This is called the *dark current* of the device, and the average (dc value) is identified by the symbol I_d. The dark current is but one of the unwanted signals that compete with the signal current and detract from the role of a perfectly linear relationship between the detector output and the luminous flux input. Other sources that impair the relationship are the noise sources. Noise sources have various origins and are characterized by current fluctuations. Although the dark current is often expressed as a dc term, in reality it is random in nature. Other noise sources, such as photon noise (due to the random arrival nature of photons) and thermal (or Johnson) noise, more often dominate. Those noise sources are not only generated at the detector but are also present in all the ensuing signal processing. These various noise sources will be dealt with later; however, it is important that the detector output be immediately amplified (or preamplified) by a high-performance, low-

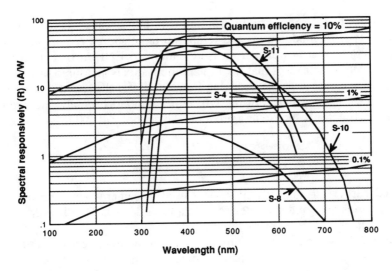

Figure 6.20 Spectral response of typical photodetectors.

noise amplifier. This has the impact of amplifying only the detector output (both detector signal and detector noise) and the noise picked up at the input to the preamplifier to an output level whereby later introductions of noise by the remainder of the signal processing has an insignificant impact on the overall system signal-to-noise ratio. The gain in the preamplifier is a careful selection to give as much gain as is possible without compromising the overall bandwidth at this stage and without limiting the dynamic range of the ensuing signal processing. The latter is often such a constraint that today most signal processing is digital alleviating somewhat the analog constraints.

This brings us in a logical progression to three critical system performance parameters: (1) signal-to-noise ratio; (2) *equivalent noise input* (ENI); and (3) *noise equivalent power* (NEP). The signal-to-noise ratio is expressed in decibels in a given bandwidth. The bandwidth is important, in that many noise sources are near white noise and therefore have a flat amplitude *versus* frequency characteristic. By limiting the bandwidth of the device the higher-frequency content of the noise is removed, resulting in a better SNR figure. Lowering the bandwidth however lowers the spatial response of the detector, resulting in a blurring of the displayed image and an overall loss in system MTF. The compromise therefore has to be judicious. The bandwidth selection should be to maximize signal-to-noise characteristics without compromising overall system MTF characteristics.

Equivalent noise input is the value of input flux that produces a *root mean square* (rms) signal current just equal to the rms noise current in a specified bandwidth (usually 1 Hz). It is a useful figure in determining threshold of detection characteristics but it should be interpreted carefully because parameters such as frequency, type of modulation, and temperature of source require specification. The noise equivalent power is a measure similar to ENI, in that it represents a unity SNR condition except that the radiant input flux is measured in watts. Again the frequency bandwidth, the chopping frequency, and the spectral content of the radiation must be specified. For the last, either a monochromatic radiation at the peak of the detector response or a broadband blackbody at 500 K is often selected.

6.3.2.2 IR Detectors

As stated earlier the majority of devices used in cameras covering the 3–5 and 8–14 μm bands are solid-state devices. Chapter 2 deals at length with discussions on IR detectors and detector materials.

Although the descriptive nature of the background materials and their developments is of interest, this book is concerned with the analysis of the detector and its performance as it relates to the overall performance of the camera and the total optical system of which it is a key part. Much of the analysis so far discussed under the optical detector section is pertinent as well to the analysis of infrared detectors with the appropriate change in wavelength to accommodate the particular band of interest. However, for infrared detectors we will introduce two additional commonly met parameters; detectivity and D^* (D-star). Associated with these parameters are the additional descriptors of spectral or blackbody. The following provides both the definition and the mathematical description of these parameters.

Detectivity (D) is the reciprocal of NEP and therefore is in W^{-1}. Spectral detectivity ($D(\lambda)$) and blackbody detectivity (D_{BB}) are the reciprocals of spectral and blackbody noise equivalent power, respectively. Therefore,

$$D(\lambda) = \frac{1}{\text{NEP}(\lambda)} = \frac{\mathscr{R}(\lambda)}{v_n} \tag{6.83}$$

where v_n is the rms noise voltage and $\mathscr{R}(\lambda)$ is the spectral detectivity. Furthermore,

$$D_{BB} = \frac{1}{\text{NEP}_{BB}} = \frac{\mathscr{R}_{BB}}{v_n} \tag{6.84}$$

Noise equivalent power for most IR photodetectors is proportional to the square root of the sensitive area (A_d) and the bandwidth Δf of the measuring system. Parameter D^* has been defined as a figure of merit that uses the square root of the area and bandwidth to normalize detectivity as a means of comparison. Like detectivity, spectral D^* and blackbody D^* are defined according to whether the normalization is performed on the spectral NEP or the blackbody NEP. D^* is in cm $Hz^{1/2}W^{-1}$.

$$D^*(\lambda, f_c) = \frac{A^{1/2}\Delta f^{1/2}}{NEP(\lambda)} = \frac{A^{1/2}\Delta^{1/2}\mathcal{R}(\lambda)}{v_n} \tag{6.85}$$

where f_c is the chopping frequency used in the measurement, and

$$D^*(T_{BB}, f_c) = \frac{A^{1/2}\Delta^{1/2}}{NEP_{BB}} = \frac{A^{1/2}\Delta^{1/2}\mathcal{R}_{BB}}{v_n} \tag{6.86}$$

where T_{BB} is the temperature of the blackbody.

All past discussions center around the theoretical limit of photon detectors due to noise. We discussed in earlier chapters the following sources of noise:

1. photon noise, $(v_n)_{ph}$
2. generation-recombination noise, $(v_n)_{gr}$
3. $1/f$ or modulation noise, $(v_n)_f$
4. Johnson noise, $(v_n)_J$
5. shot noise, $(v_n)_s$.

Definitions of these noises were provided earlier in Chapter 2, and hence here it is necessary only to provide the total noise in a detector as

$$(v_n)_{total} = [(v_n)_{ph}^2 + (v_n)_{gr}^2 + (v_n)_f^2 + (v_n)_J^2 + (v_n)_s^2]^{1/2} \tag{6.87}$$

For D^* and SNR, as given in Section 6.2, the image irradiance is given by

$$E_I = \frac{\pi}{4}L(R)/T^2 \tag{6.88}$$

where

$L(R)$ = radiance at range R (through the atmosphere)
T = optics T number.

Spectrally,

$$E_{I\lambda} = \frac{\pi}{4}L_\lambda(R)/T^2 \tag{6.89}$$

Now the voltage generated by the detector is given by

$$V_{rms} = \int_0^\infty \mathcal{R}_\lambda \phi_\lambda \, d\lambda \tag{6.90}$$

where

$\mathcal{R}_\lambda$ = detector spectral responsivity

ϕ_λ = spectral radiant flux in the image.

But

$$\phi_\lambda = E_{I\lambda} A_d$$

where A_d is the area of the detector. Therefore,

$$V_{rms} = \frac{\pi A_d}{4T^2} \int_0^\infty \mathcal{R}_\lambda L_\lambda \, d_\lambda \tag{6.91}$$

But the spectral responsivity is given by

$$\mathcal{R}_\lambda = D_\lambda^* \frac{V_{nrms}}{\sqrt{A_d \Delta \nu}} \tag{6.92}$$

where

V_{nrms} = rms noise voltage

D_λ^* = spectral detectivity.

Thus,

$$V_{rms} = \frac{\pi A_d}{4T^2} \frac{1}{\sqrt{A_d \Delta \nu}} V_{nrms} \int_0^\infty D_\lambda^* \, L_\lambda(R) \, d\lambda$$

or

$$SNR \equiv \frac{V_{rms}}{V_{nrms}} = \frac{\pi}{4T^2} \sqrt{A_d/\Delta \nu} \int_0^\infty D_\lambda^* \, L_\lambda(R) \, d\lambda \tag{6.93}$$

Note that the SNR is dependent on the inverse square of the T number and correspondingly proportional to the inverse square of the F number of the system. It is also directly dependent on D-star.

6.3.2.3 Common Detector Arrangements

In FLIRs detectors are arranged as full arrays (for staring FLIRs), columns (for parallel scanned FLIRs), or as discrete singular (or in small number) elements (for serial scan arrays). An example of the use of a column array is the common module FLIR. The industry is still arguing over whether more performance is achieved by using parallel scanned devices or serial scan devices. The expectation is that, having more elements and longer dwell times, the performance of a parallel scan device would be much more sensitive. In reality, the increase in performance is offset by the physical size of these arrays, and the loss in F number of these systems seems to offset the gains.

The SPRITE detector moves away from discrete devices in the serial scan sensors. SPRITE is chosen over delineated HgCdTe detector elements because the effect of multielement with *time delay and integration* (TDI) is achieved using a SPRITE with a single preamplifier and no delay lines. As it is a frequent device in modern FLIRs, we will take a closer look at this device and its MTF.

The principle of the SPRITE operation takes advantage of the fact that the free carriers in the HgCdTe drift through the material in a predictable fashion in the presence of electric field with a drift velocity V_d of

$$V_d = \mu_a E \tag{6.94}$$

where

μ_a = free carrier mobility
E = electric field.

When coherent target radiant energy is focused and scanned across the material, an enhancement or additive process occurs by matching the drift velocity to the scanned scene velocity, in that the coherent energy continues to generate free carriers. An 8–12 μm system is modeled using a free carrier lifetime of 2.5 μs, which translates to 7 TDI in a SPRITE bar for the 8–12 μm material.

6.3.2.4 MTF of a Sensor Using the SPRITE Detector

As the spot is being summed as it travels through the SPRITE bar, it also has a diffusion spreading which in effect blurs the image and reduces the SPRITE MTF. This is modeled as follows:

$$\text{SPRITE MTF}_D = \frac{\sin(\pi \nu L)}{\pi \nu L} \cdot \frac{1}{1 + \nu^2 Q^2} \tag{6.95}$$

where

> ν = frequency (cycles/mrad)
> L = length of readout region (mrad)
> Q = diffusion length (mrad).

The first term is the common sinc function with the second being the MTF SPRITE diffusion term. Typical free carrier lifetimes are on the order of a few microseconds, and free carrier mobility can be on the order of a few hundred cm²/V − s. Diffusion spreading can therefore be around 10 μm.

6.3.3 Signal Processing

When a detector in a FLIR system is irradiated it produces an output signal voltage. Of course much happens to this signal before it is finally ready to drive a display. Usually each detector has its own preamplifier to amplify the signal immediately. Also many different kinds of electronic filtering and boosting may take place, which simply means that different frequencies within the signal are amplified by different amounts. The process of time delay and integration is standard for serial scan systems. Parallel scan systems with a standard video display will require some sort of multiplexing, whereby the simultaneous signals from the multiple detectors on different scan lines are arranged into the proper sequence for a single video signal.

For the purposes of modeling the system, all of the processes are usually described by MTFs that affect the modulation in the signal passed to the display. These electronic MTFs will be functions of temporal frequency, but this frequency, ν, is related to spatial frequency in the scan direction in the image (customarily designated the x direction), ν_x:

$$\nu = \frac{\alpha}{t_d}\nu_x \tag{6.96}$$

where

> α = detector angular subtense (mrad)
> t_d = detector dwell time (s),

The reader should be forewarned that many of the signal processing techniques discussed do not appear to satisfy the conditions for linear systems that were outlined in Section 6.1. However, it is always possible to define an MTF as the ratio of output modulation to input modulation of a sinusoidal signal. If the conditions for linearity are not satisfied, then the MTF is not just the Fourier transform of the *point spread function* (PSF). For example some of these processes actually have MTF values greater than unity at some frequencies, but this property does not imply that the corresponding PSF has zero width. Unfortunately it cannot be shown in the case of nonlinear systems that the total MTF is the product of the component MTFs, yet it is still common practice to make this assumption. Perhaps we should not be overly concerned about this as the electronic response is seldom the limiting factor within the system.

6.3.3.1 ac Coupling

Typically the detectors in a FLIR system are ac coupled. That is, the signal from the detector preamplifier is sent to the rest of the system through the circuit shown in Figure 6.21. This circuit acts as a filter to block any dc (constant) component in the signal: it is a high-pass filter. Its effects on other frequency components depend on the time constant of the circuit, which in turn depends on the values of resistance, R, and capacitance, C. This method is used because the contrast in the received IR radiance is very low. In effect the system will respond to differences in received radiance rather than directly to radiance, and it is this difference that we wish to amplify with later stages in the processing. The subsequent amplification is usually operator controlled at least in part by a gain setting. Also usually a level setting is available that adds a constant voltage everywhere before the signal is displayed.

Like any technique, ac coupling is not an unmixed blessing. Some of its attendant problems can be seen by considering the response of the ac coupling

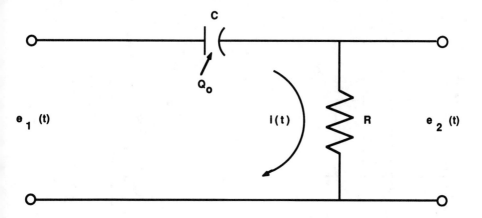

Figure 6.21 ac coupling circuit.

circuit to a simple rectangular pulse, assuming the initial charge on the capacitor is 0, shown in Figure 6.22. There is zero output as the constant zero portion of the signal preceding the pulse scans across the detector. When the signal change (front edge of the pulse) hits the detector there is a large output response. But as the constant part of the rectangular pulse crosses the detector, the output decays back toward 0. How fast the output decays depends on the time constant. This decay is known as *dc droop*. Then when the back edge of the pulse hits the detector, there is a sharp downward response, which because of the previous droop throws the output negative. Finally as the constant zero input following the pulse scans across the detector, the output again decays toward 0. The negative response and subsequent decay up toward 0 is known as *undershoot*. Making the time constant of the circuit long will minimize dc droop but make the undershoot recovery slower as well. In fact we can show that the area under the curve is the same above and below the axis.

Still another defect is inherent in ac coupling if several lines are being scanned at once (parallel scan); this could be called *channel nonuniformity*. The preceding description assumed that the initial capacitor charge was 0, but as the system operates the capacitor actually accumulates charge. This accumulated charge is likely to be different in each channel (each of the lines in the parallel scan) because it depends on the previous history of the signal in that channel. Therefore, instead of each channel starting from 0 as shown in Figure 6.22, different channels start from unpredictable levels. Then when two channels scan simultaneously through a single large uniform target, they can give totally different responses. The outcome is that the uniform target will appear nonuniform line to line on the display. This defect is totally independent of, and additive to, any inherent nonuniformities that may exist between channels because the preamplifiers have not been properly adjusted to give matching responses. We might note here that even serial scanning

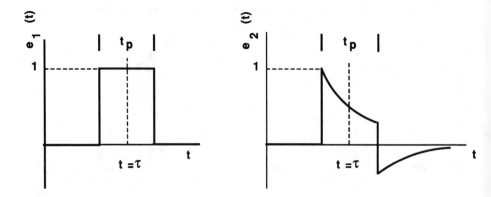

Figure 6.22 dc droop and undershoot for an ac coupled FLIR.

systems often scan more than one line at a time (they are really serial-parallel scan), so they would suffer from the same problem.

6.3.3.2 dc Restoration

Channel nonuniformity can be corrected by dc restoration. In this technique all the channels are scanned across a thermally uniform reference source within the system during an inactive portion of the scan. In other words, the scan really continues past the HFOV of the system to see this reference. During this portion of the scan the coupling capacitors of all the channels are shorted to ground so that they all come to a common charge set by the reference source. Thus all channels will start the next scan across the image with the same charge and therefore the same voltage level. The penalty for this correction is a decrease in scan efficiency: for a fixed frame rate each detector gets less dwell time on the image.

6.3.3.3 Time Delay and Integration

A common processing technique for serial scanned detector arrays is TDI. As the image is scanned across a row of individual detectors their signals are delayed and summed by an integrating delay line, as in Figure 6.23. The delay in the delay line

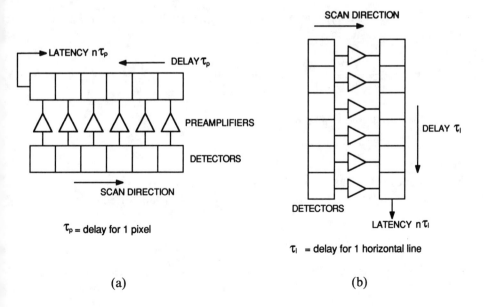

Figure 6.23 Horizontal (a) and vertical (b) time delay and integration of FLIR signal.

is synchronized with the scan rate so that the signal from a single point in the image is built up coherently. On the other hand, because the noise from the individual detectors is uncorrelated, it sums incoherently. The result is that the signal increases linearly with the number of detectors, N, whereas the noise increases only as $\sqrt{N}$. Therefore, the signal-to-noise ratio increases as $\sqrt{N}$, as does the effective detectivity of the array.

The preceding discussion might be somewhat misleading, because the same number of detectors scanned in parallel, rather than serially with TDI, would also show an improvement in SNR by a factor of $\sqrt{N}$ over that of a single detector. This improvement comes about because, with more lines being scanned simultaneously, the dwell time for each detector can be longer, resulting in a reduced noise bandwidth. However, for a serial scanned array the detectors need not be matched, as is the case for a parallel scanned array.

6.3.3.4 Electronics MTF

The MTF of the electronic filtering can usually be approximated by a combination of three general types of filters: the high-pass filter of Figure 6.21, the low-pass filter, and the all-pass lead (see Figure 6.24).

6.3.3.5 High-Pass Filter

The MTF of the first type is of immediate interest because it describes the ac coupling:

$$\text{MTF}_E = \frac{\nu/\nu_c}{\sqrt{1 + (\nu/\nu_c)^2}} \tag{6.97}$$

with the cutoff frequency given by

$$\nu_c = 1/(2\pi RC) \tag{6.98}$$

This frequency is the 3 dB point, or when the MTF $= .707$. Note that the function in (6.97) goes to 0 when $\nu = 0$, illustrating the dc blocking effect.

6.3.3.6 Low-Pass Filter

Most electronic components respond well at lower frequencies but degrade in performance as frequency continues to increase. These may be modeled by the

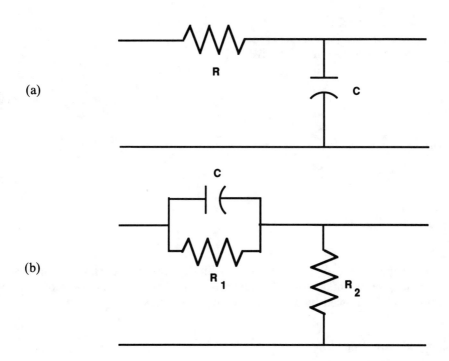

Figure 6.24 Low-pass filter (a) and all-pass lead (b).

low-pass filter of Figure 6.24. For example, the detectors themselves have a finite response time and will not respond fully to an excessively rapid change in signal. The MTF for this type filter is

$$\text{MTF}_E = \frac{1}{\sqrt{1 + (\nu/\nu_c)^2}} \qquad (6.99)$$

where ν_c is still given by (6.98) and still represents the 3 dB point. This MTF has a value of unity at $\nu = 0$, but approaches 0 as ν becomes much larger than ν_c.

One might wonder what values of R and C to use for the calculation of ν_c, if the circuit in Figure 6.24 is just a model for some electronic component. Fortunately the cutoff frequency in this case can be directly related to the response time of the component, t_r, obviating the need for any R or C values:

$$\nu_c = 1/t_r \qquad (6.100)$$

6.3.3.7 All-Pass Lead

The all-pass lead has an MTF given by

$$\text{MTF}_E = \frac{1 + (\nu/\nu_c)^2}{\sqrt{G^2 + (\nu/\nu_c)^2}} \tag{6.101}$$

with

$$\nu_c = 1/(2\pi R_1 C) \tag{6.102}$$

$$G = \frac{R_1 + R_2}{R_2} \tag{6.103}$$

This is sometimes used in combination with the other two to simulate the response of some components. Lloyd, [4] suggests boosting circuits can be modeled by an all-pass lead followed by a double-RC low-pass filter.

6.3.3.8 Boosting Circuits

Another standard form for the boost transfer function is

$$\text{MTF}_E = 1 + \frac{K - 1}{2} [1 - \cos(\pi\nu/\nu_m)] \tag{6.104}$$

where K and ν_m are parameters that control the amplitude and frequency of the boost.

6.4 DISPLAYS

The final system interface with the human observer is the display. Care must be taken at this point not to undo the advantages provided by good design in the rest of the system. Basically, the display must take the electric signal from the system electronics and convert it into an image for the human operator to view: an image with good resolution at luminance levels sufficiently high for the task at hand. We will concentrate on the two most common (by far) display devices: light-emitting diodes and cathode ray tubes.

6.4.1 LED

The parallel-scan, parallel-video FLIR systems typically have a display consisting of LEDs directly connected each to an individual detector and scanned by the same mirror that scans the image across the detectors. This scanned LED display is viewed through an eyepiece, so that the system is somewhat like a telescopic sight with the scanned LED plane replacing the real image plane. The image angular size is

$$\delta_I = d_I/f_e \tag{6.105}$$

where

f_e = eyepiece EFL
d_I = image linear size in LED plane.

Usually the d_I can be found by expressing the object size as a fraction of the VFOV and then taking that fractional part of the full vertical size of the scanned area of the LED array.

Although LEDs are fast-response, low-power devices, they have the disadvantages of relatively low maximum luminance (≤ 70 fL) and low resolution (limited by physical size). The major advantage of the parallel-scan, parallel-video FLIR is the great simplicity of conversion to output image, and the major disadvantage is the restriction to a single viewer looking through an eyepiece.

As a simplification the LED can be treated as a sharply defined, uniform source. In other words, its response is a rect function in each dimension. The corresponding MTF is a product of sinc functions just as for the array of detectors:

$$\mathrm{MTF}_D = \frac{\sin(\pi a \nu_x)}{\pi a \nu_x} \cdot \frac{\sin(\pi b \nu_y)}{\pi b \nu_y} \equiv \mathrm{sinc}(a\nu_x) \cdot \mathrm{sinc}(b\nu_y) \tag{6.106}$$

where

a = LED size in the x dimension
b = LED size in the y dimension.

This function goes to 0 at $a\nu_x = 1$, so $\nu_x = 1/a$ (or $\nu_y = 1/b$) represents a limiting frequency.

6.4.2 CRT

CRTs represent the most mature and commonly used display technology. In a CRT an electron beam is scanned in a raster pattern across the face of the tube that contains a phosphor, to convert the beam intensity into a visible light pattern through the process of electrofluorescence. The standard 2:1 interlace scanning pattern paints every other line across the screen in what is called *one field*. The next field fills in the intermediate lines. Two fields constitute a complete frame or complete displayed image on the screen. United States standards specify 30 frames or 60 fields per second, each frame with about 490 horizontally painted lines (known as *active* lines).

6.4.2.1 Transfer Characteristics

A typical CRT has not quite as fast a response as an LED and uses more power; on the other hand, it could have luminances up to several thousand footlamberts, a finer resolution, and can be viewed by many observers simultaneously. A CRT display in general can be characterized by a transfer curve like that in Figure 6.25. When log display luminance is plotted *versus* log signal strength, a linear region is found between threshold signal and saturation signal. The slope of the linear region is known as the display gamma. For signals below the threshold, zero luminance is produced on the display (because there is a threshold for the on-set of fluorescence); for signals above saturation only maximum luminance is produced. Therefore, the useful operating region is between threshold and saturation. As a matter of practicality, the display luminance is never exactly 0, even if the emitted luminance is, because there will always be some reflected ambient luminance.

Usually the display gamma and threshold signal can be varied by the user, or at least by the system designer (gain and level settings or contrast and brightness settings). The higher the gamma value is the more contrast can be displayed between two given objects with different signal strengths. However, such contrast stretch must be balanced against the dynamic range: from the figure we can see that a greater slope of the linear region implies a smaller useful region of signal strengths. One way to specify dynamic range is in shades of gray reproducible by the display. One gray shade is defined electronically as a 3 dB increment in signal strength (corresponding to a factor of $\sqrt{2}$).

A general equation [5] relates the display luminance, L, at a point to the corresponding signal strength, V, in the linear region:

$$L = k(V - V_T)^\gamma \tag{6.107}$$

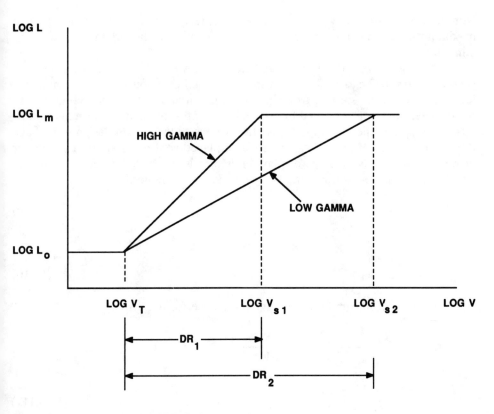

Figure 6.25 Transfer curve for CRT display.

where

$$k = \text{proportionality constant}$$
$$V_T = \text{threshold signal}$$
$$\gamma = \text{display gamma.}$$

From the definition of dynamic range, it must also be true that

$$V_S = \sqrt{2^N} V_T \tag{6.108}$$

where

$$V_S = \text{saturation signal}$$
$$N = \text{number of gray shades in the dynamic range.}$$

Note that N does not have to be an integer; indeed, it will be uncommon for the maximum usable signal to be exactly a whole number of factors of $\sqrt{2}$ times the minimum.

The values of k, V_T, and V_S are seldom known to the system designer, and yet we would still like to be able to say something definite about displayed luminance levels and contrasts, starting from just information about the signal being sent to the display. Therefore, it is helpful to work with ratios of many of these quantities. Also we may use one quantity that is often known to the system designer: average display luminance. The greatest range of displayed contrast is allowed (above or below average) if the average display luminance is set to the middle gray shade, which is also the geometric mean between the two extremes:

$$L_A = k(V_A - V_T)^\gamma \qquad (6.109)$$

with

$$V_A = \sqrt{2^{N/2}} V_T \qquad (6.110)$$

Then the ratio of maximum to average luminance for the display is

$$L_S/L_A = \frac{k(V_S - V_T)^\gamma}{k(V_A - V_T)^\gamma} = \left(\frac{V_S/V_T - 1}{V_A/V_T - 1}\right)^\gamma$$

$$= \left(\frac{\sqrt{2^N} - 1}{\sqrt{2^{N/2}} - 1}\right)^\gamma = (2^{N/4} + 1)^\gamma \qquad (6.111)$$

If we assume that the system designer knows the maximum display luminance and the average display luminance, the latter of which is determined by system settings, then (6.111) allows that designer to solve for either display gamma, γ, or dynamic range in gray shades, N, depending on which one is known:

$$\gamma = \frac{\log(L_S/L_A)}{\log(2^{N/4} + 1)} \qquad (6.112)$$

$$N = \frac{4\log[(L_S/L_A)^{1/\gamma} - 1]}{\log 2} \qquad (6.113)$$

These equations justify the statement made earlier that a trade-off is to be made between display gamma and display dynamic range. Either shows a monotonic decrease with the increase of the other. In fact, if the dynamic range is large (so that the ± 1 is negligible in the two equations), then there is an exact inverse relationship. We should note here that either natural or common logarithms can be used in (6.112) or (6.113), as long as the same type is used in both the denominator and the numerator. Also note that the maximum luminance used in the equations does not have to be saturation, but rather simply the maximum (white) level corresponding to the N shades of gray.

To give some idea of the numerical values involved, we may examine the RS-170 standard for monochrome studio facilities in the United States. In this standard, the picture signal range from a black level at .075 V to a white level of 1 V. This range is all within the linear region of the display: black is above zero luminance and white is below saturation. This corresponds to a dynamic range of about 7.5 gray steps; experiments have shown that without at least 7 shades of gray, human recognition performance is degraded. At the output end, the standard calls for the monitor to have a white level of at least 15 fL and a brightness ratio (white to black) of at least 30:1. These values used in (6.112) imply a gamma value of at least $\gamma = 1.1$; higher gamma values are obtained if the brightness ratio of the display is above the minimum specified. In fact it is common for displays in ordinary television to have gamma values in excess of 2, so that the overall gamma of the system is just above unity. This adjustment is because of the usual dark surrounding conditions in which the picture is viewed, necessitating an enhanced contrast in the image to give a realistic picture [5]. Of course, if the video signal is from a FLIR, there is no "natural" image for comparison, and the system designer is somewhat freer in the choice of a display gamma: a higher gamma will increase the detectability of hot spots, but at the expense of recognizability of extended objects if the gray shades drop too low.

6.4.2.2 *Image Size*

Image angular size is generally controlled by how far away from the screen the observer is, and for small angles it is

$$\delta_I \approx d_I/D_o \qquad (6.114)$$

where

d_I = image linear size on CRT face
D_o = operator distance from screen.

From this equation it would seem that the observer could enhance acquisition probability by moving ever closer to the screen. However, one's proximity is limited by the near point of the eye, and at very close distances the raster pattern itself becomes objectionable. Experiments with observers who were free to vary their viewing distance from a standard TV display showed that they tended to pick distances just far enough away to make the raster unnoticeable (one raster line subtending about 1 minute of arc) [6]. This amounts to a display that subtends about 8° vertically, or an observer distance about four times the display diagonal for a standard 4:3 aspect ratio.

6.4.2.3 Resolution

Ideally one would like to have an MTF curve for a CRT display, but such is seldom published or even measured by manufacturers. Instead a number of single-value resolution measures might be given. Under reasonable assumptions, each of these measures can be used to generate an MTF curve.

The assumption universally applied is that the electron scanning beam and the resulting light spot on the screen have circularly symmetric Gaussian shapes. Then the spot luminance around the center is given by

$$\mathcal{L} = \frac{1}{2\pi\sigma^2} \exp\left(-\frac{x^2 + y^2}{2\sigma^2}\right) \tag{6.115}$$

This is also the point spread function of the device, leading to an MTF of

$$\text{MTF}_D = \exp[-2\pi^2\sigma^2(\nu_x^2 + \nu_y^2)] \tag{6.116}$$

Both of these can be factored into two independent parts

$$\mathcal{L} = \mathcal{L}_x \mathcal{L}_y \tag{6.117}$$

$$\text{MTF}_D = \text{MTF}_{Dx}\text{MTF}_{Dy} \tag{6.118}$$

with

$$\mathcal{L}_u \equiv \frac{1}{\sqrt{2\pi}\sigma} \exp\left(-\frac{u^2}{2\sigma^2}\right) \tag{6.119}$$

$$\text{MTF}_{Du} \equiv \exp(-2\pi^2\sigma^2\nu_u^2) \tag{6.120}$$

The first resolution measure is called the *shrinking line raster resolution*. In this test, the line spacing in the raster scan itself (no image) is shrunk until an observer can no longer detect the individual scan lines. This seems to occur at a reasonably constant, small value of luminance ripple for all observers. Larger spot sizes (larger σ values) lead to larger line separations for the occurrence of this condition. So poor resolution displays are characterized by large values of shrinking raster line separation, and high resolution by small values. The appropriate line separation, s, is near 2σ, and it is common practice to take

$$\sigma = .54s \qquad (6.121)$$

So specification of s can be used to construct a Gaussian CRT MTF like (6.116) with σ given by (6.121).

The other very common specification is television resolution or the TV limiting response. In this case a test pattern like that of Figure 6.26 is viewed on the display. The tapering bar patterns are examined for the closest spacing that can just be resolved (units on the pattern are TV lines/picture height, where two TV lines are

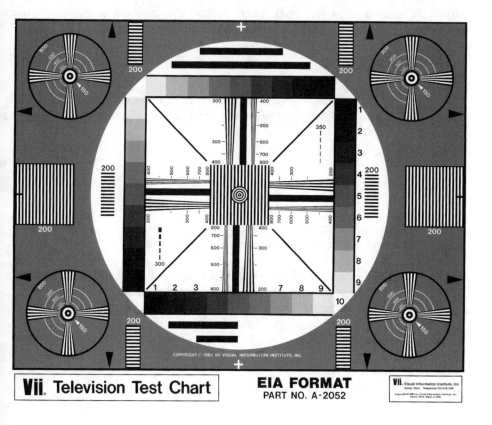

Figure 6.26 Test pattern for TV limiting resolution.

equivalent to one cycle). The bar pattern generally fades out at a line spacing (black-white adjacent) of about 1.18σ. In other words we have a limiting bar pattern period, p, of 2.36σ:

$$\sigma = .42p \tag{6.122}$$

This is around the 3% point on the MTF curve. As with shrinking raster line separation, because the TV limiting resolution at least roughly fixes σ, an MTF curve of form (6.116) may be generated. In performing this test one must be careful to isolate the display performance from the rest of the television system: all components contribute to the final resolution seen on the screen. However if the other components have much higher resolution than the CRT, then the test described will essentially measure display performance. It should also be noted that, although a TV system is required for the test, once the display MTF is established the same curve can be used no matter what sort of system the display is subsequently used in.

6.4.3 System Magnification

The overall system magnification can be ascertained only after the display has been considered. It can be defined just like the angular magnification of a telescopic sight:

$$m \equiv \delta_I/\delta_O \tag{6.123}$$

where

δ_I = displayed image angular size
δ_O = object angular size subtended at entrance pupil.

The parallel-scan, parallel-display FLIR systems are similar to telescopic sights in that the final view is through an eyepiece. Usually it is convenient to consider the object to be the whole field of view to calculate magnification. The image vertical angular size is approximately given by

$$\delta_I \approx y_s/f_e \tag{6.124}$$

where y_s is the vertical linear size of scanned area. So

$$m = \frac{y_s}{f_e \, \text{VFOV}} \tag{6.125}$$

Of course if the angles become large then $2\tan^{-1}(y_s/2f_e)$ must be used in place of the ratio y_s/f_e. One can find y_s by multiplying the number of detectors times their vertical size (times two for a 2:1 interlace):

$$y_s = (2)N_d b/r_o \tag{6.126}$$

where

N_d = number of detectors in vertical array
b = vertical detector size
r_o = overscan ratio.

Note that the factor of two applies to the 2:1 interlace scan.

Another display arrangement that is very like the LED array is a small CRT viewed through an eyepiece. The only difference would be that y_s must be the vertical dimension of the scanned area on the tube face. For example a 1-inch diameter CRT might have a scanned area of only 16 mm diagonal, which implies y_s = 9.6 mm for 4:3 aspect ratio.

When a CRT is viewed directly we may combine (6.114) and (6.123), using the vertical field of view as an object again:

$$m = \frac{d_v}{D_o(\text{VFOV})} \tag{6.127}$$

where d_v is the display vertical size. As before, an arc tangent must be used in place of the simple ratio of lengths if the angle subtended by the display at the observer's position is not small.

It is important to bear in mind that system magnification is *not* in general the same thing as magnification of the system optics. Although the two are related, the relationship is not simple, and it depends on how the final image is displayed.

6.5 SUMMARY PERFORMANCE MEASURES

There are a number of summary performance measures for characterizing the performance of the system as a whole.

6.5.1 MTF

The system modulation transfer function is perhaps the most basic system measure. Yet it is often difficult even to prove the existence of such a function for some of the systems we have been considering. Certainly there is room for doubt that the conditions for linear systems treatment are satisfied in the case of ac-coupled FLIRs or systems with contrast-stretched displays ($\gamma > 1$). This doubt is made more substantial when we try to design a test for measuring system MTF. Presumably we could start with a test pattern sinusoidal in radiance (for FLIRs) or luminance (for TV) with a measured modulation. Then we could measure the luminance modulation in the displayed image. The output modulation divided by the input modulation would be the MTF value at that particular spatial frequency. Aside from the difficulty of the modulation measurements, which would require a radiometer-photometer, we note that in many of the systems mentioned previously we would find some MTF values greater than unity.

Such logical difficulties have not prevented many analysts from using the system MTF concept for ac-coupled FLIRs. Instead of measuring the system MTF, they commonly use the product of the more familiar component MTFs. Then it is simply assumed that this factor reduces the "received" ΔT to a value effective in producing the signal-to-noise ratio in the image of a periodic target. Because television systems are often set with $\gamma \approx 1$ to produce a natural looking picture, system MTF can make sense for these too.

6.5.2 TV-Limiting Resolution

This measure was introduced earlier as a way to characterize displays. However, as noted there, it really characterizes the performance of a whole TV system, camera through display. Under good lighting conditions the resolution may be limited by the display, but as the light level decreases, TV-limiting resolution will drop off because of the camera and other system components. The whole system then could be usefully characterized by a limiting resolution *versus* (camera) faceplate illumination curve. Figure 6.27 shows typical curves. We can see that this figure implies a system MTF curve that varies with illumination. This type of limiting resolution curve is used not only for TV but also for image intensifiers, image converters, and other electronic imaging devices. Because all the curves bend to become flat at high illumination levels, this value is often quoted as a single number resolution measure for the system.

The frequency in many of these graphs is expressed in TV lines per picture height. This may be converted to cycles/mm (in the plane of the displayed image) by dividing by twice the display height in mm; the factor of 2 stems from 2 TV lines = 1 cycle. Or if the frequency value is divided by twice the vertical field of view in milliradians, we obtain cycles/mrad in object space.

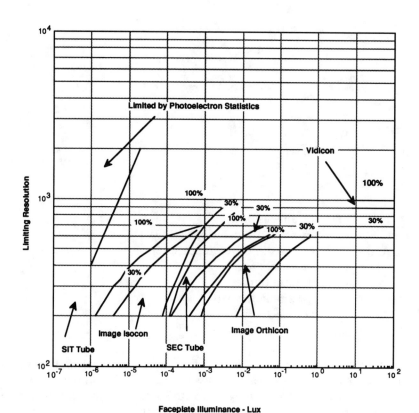

Figure 6.27 Typical limiting resolutions *versus* faceplate illumination.

6.5.3 Noise-Equivalent Temperature Difference

We now arrive at performance measures specifically for FLIRs, the first of which is the *noise-equivalent temperature difference* (NETD). It may be defined as the blackbody target-to-background temperature difference in a standard test pattern that produces a peak signal-to-rms-noise ratio of unity at the output of an electronic reference filter. The test pattern consists of a large square, uniform, hotter target on a uniform, cooler background. This square target should be at least several times larger than the system IFOV. The peak signal typically is read from a scope display of a single line scan through the target, and an rms voltmeter can be used for the noise measurement.

Although we refer the reader to Lloyd [4] for details of the derivation, we set down here the result obtained under reasonable assumptions:

$$\text{NETD} = \frac{\pi \sqrt{ab\Delta\nu_R}}{\alpha\beta A_E \tau_o D^*(\lambda_p)\dfrac{\Delta M}{\Delta T}} \tag{6.128}$$

with

$$\frac{\Delta M}{\Delta T} \equiv \int \frac{\partial M_\lambda}{\partial T}(T_B)\frac{D^*(\lambda)}{D^*(\lambda_p)}\, d\lambda \tag{6.129}$$

where

$$
\begin{aligned}
a, b &= \text{detector dimensions} \\
\alpha, \beta &= \text{detector angular dimensions (IFOV)} \\
\Delta\nu_R &= \text{noise bandwidth of reference filter} \\
A_E &= \text{entrance pupil area} \\
\tau_o &= \text{optics transmittance} \\
D^*(\lambda_p) &= \text{peak spectral detectivity} \\
D^*(\lambda) &= \text{spectral detectivity} \\
T_B &= \text{background temperature.}
\end{aligned}
$$

The integral in (6.128) must extend far enough in wavelength to cover the spectral band of the detector. This expression for NETD, although complicated, is fairly certain because we are dealing only with physical components whose behavior is well understood. NETD is a single value rather than a curve and may be used for rough estimates of SNR from the FLIR for large targets:

$$\text{SNR} \approx \Delta T/\text{NETD} \tag{6.130}$$

where ΔT is the "received" temperature difference. Most good FLIRs can be expected to have NETD values of a few tenths of a degree Kelvin.

There are many drawbacks to using just NETD as a FLIR system figure of merit. It does not characterize much of the system because it is measured before the display. Also it cannot be realistically related to field performance. Lloyd suggests that it is more useful for tracking the history of performance of a single system rather than even a tool for comparing two different systems.

6.5.4 Minimum Resolvable Temperature Difference

The most widely used FLIR system performance measure is *minimum resolvable temperature difference* (MRTD), sometimes written just MRT. This quantity is measured using a test pattern like that shown in Figure 6.28. Again blackbody radiation is assumed from the hotter bars and cooler background. Starting from 0, the temperature difference is increased until the largest bar pattern can just be confidently resolved by an observer with normal vision viewing the display. This temperature difference becomes the MRTD value for that lowest spatial frequency. Then the temperature difference is increased again until the next largest bar pattern can be resolved, and so on. In this manner a curve of MRTD *versus* spatial frequency is mapped out. Typically it would appear as shown in Figure 6.29.

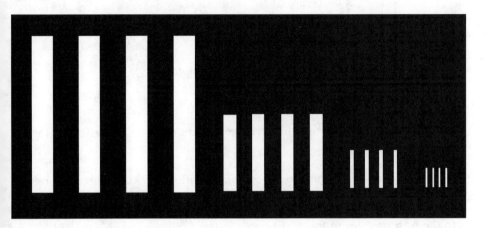

Figure 6.28 Test pattern for MRTD.

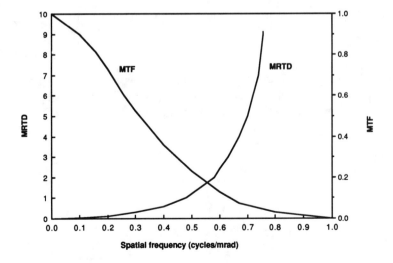

Figure 6.29 Typical FLIR MTF and MRTD curves.

MRTD of a system can also be derived in terms of the system parameters, but in this case assumptions must be made as well about the human observer, such as the SNR value required for a given probability of detection. Some of these assumptions are tenuous at best, but without them MRTD would be impossible to calculate. The result is

$$\text{MRTD}(\nu_x) = \frac{3 \text{ NETD } \sqrt{\rho \beta \nu_x}}{\text{MTF}_S(\nu_x) \sqrt{t_e} \text{FR}}$$

(6.131)

where

$$\nu_x = \text{spatial frequency in the } x \text{ direction}$$
$$\text{MTF}_S = \text{system MTF}$$
$$t_e = \text{eye integration time}$$
$$\text{FR} = \text{frame rate}$$
$$\rho = \text{ratio converting displayed noise bandwidth to that effective for the eye [4].}$$

Some assumptions about the eye are contained within (6.131) as it stands, but we can see that still other values characteristic to the eye are required to evaluate the MRTD. These are really very difficult to know with any degree of certainty. Most often the uncertainties in the derivation are avoided by measuring the MRTD by using the defining test described previously. Still, (6.131) and (6.128) do give some idea of trade-offs that can be made or the effects of system changes on overall performance.

If the displayed noise is white, then the ratio ρ reduces to

$$\rho = \nu / \Delta \nu_R$$

(6.132)

where ν is the temporal frequency of the target. This temporal frequency can be converted to spatial frequency in the x direction (cycles/mrad) by using the detector dwell time, t_d (how fast a point scans across a detector):

$$\nu = \frac{\alpha}{t_d} \nu_x$$

(6.133)

So

$$\text{MRTD}(\nu_x) = \frac{3(\text{NETD}/\Delta \nu_R) \sqrt{\alpha \beta} \, \nu_x}{\text{MTF}(\nu_x) \sqrt{t_e t_d} \text{FR}}$$

(6.134)

This equation is often preferred because it uses the NETD normalized by the bandwidth at which it was measured and because dependence on ν_x is made more explicit.

MRTD represents a considerably improved measure over NETD because it not only indicates the low-frequency temperature sensitivity, as does the latter, but it also shows the high-frequency performance, where system resolution is a limiting factor. The curve of Figure 6.29 indicates that there is a limiting spatial frequency and that it occurs in the region where $MTF_S \rightarrow 0$, which is also evident from (6.131). Although periodic patterns at frequencies higher than this cutoff may be impossible to resolve, real targets are aperiodic and may be detected even when considerably smaller than the cutoff period (or even half the cutoff period). As Lloyd [4] points out, MRTD is useful for predicting recognition performance but does not relate in any simple way to practical detection tasks.

6.5.5 Minimum Detectable Temperature Difference

A performance measure intended to relate more closely to practical detection is the *minimum detectable temperature difference* (MDTD). This measure is not as widely used or accepted as MRTD.

MDTD is measured with test patterns similar to the NETD pattern: a hotter blackbody square on a cooler blackbody background. Only for the MDTD test, squares of various sizes must be available. Then for any size square target (side w) the MDTD is the minimum temperature difference that allows an observer to detect the target, with unlimited decision time and no search (target position is known).

Under assumptions similar to those for the MRTD derivation, MDTD can be calculated to be

$$MDTD(\nu_x) = \frac{1.5\sqrt{2}\,MTF_S(\nu_x)}{\overline{I(x,y)}}\,MRTD(\nu_x) \tag{6.135}$$

where $\overline{I(x,y)}$ is the average normalized image intensity. That is, the effective temperature difference seen by the eye is $\overline{I(x,y)}\Delta T$, when ΔT is the actual blackbody temperature difference in the test pattern. Calculating this average intensity can be difficult, but if the target angular size is small compared to the system IFOV, we have simply

$$\overline{I(x,y)} = \frac{\alpha\beta}{HIFOV \cdot VIFOV} \tag{6.136}$$

Spatial frequency for the square targets is taken as $(2w)^{-1}$.

It may be noted that, because MRTD contains $1/MTF_S$, the system MTF in (6.135) cancels out so there is no absolute cutoff frequency. This means that no target is too small to be detected if it is hot enough. Once it is smaller than the resolution element of the system, however, it is certainly too small to recognize because it will appear only as a bright spot with no shape or detail evident.

REFERENCES

1. E.L. O'Neill, *Introduction to Statistical Optics*, Addison-Wesley Publishing Co., Reading, MA, 1963, pp. 95–99.
2. L. Levi, *Applied Optics*, John Wiley and Sons, New York, 1968, p. 457.
3. W. Wolfe, "Optical-Mechanical Scanning Techniques and Devices," in *The Infrared Handbook*, Office of Naval Research, Washington, DC, 1978, pp. 10-1–10-32.
4. J.M. Lloyd, *Thermal Imaging Systems*, Plenum Press, New York, 1975.
5. W.N. Sproson, *Colour Science in Television and Display Systems*, Adam Hilger Ltd., Bristol, England, 1983.
6. L.M. Biberman, "Image Quality," in *Perception of Displayed Information*, Plenum Press, New York, 1973, pp. 67–68.

Chapter 7
The Human Observer

Throughout most of history the battlefield was observed by the unaided eye. Then came the spyglass, optical sights, TV, and infrared cameras. With this growth in the aids to vision came greater demands placed on the observer. Today the observer may be required to interpret battlefield imagery in real time, when time is crucial and correct interpretations are critical, or to interpret satellite imagery taken in the past at some remote spot. In either case the quality of the imagery must match the optical task to be performed, whether it is simply counting the number of vehicles in a field or the analysis of some complex structure. The need for high-quality imagery places certain requirements on the optical aids to vision. The interpretation of this imagery is a function of the characteristics of the human visual system. The imagery should not be a limiting factor in this interpretation, although it often may be due to circumstances beyond our control. But how good should the imagery be? To understand this we must know something about the characteristics of the eye, and the eye-brain interaction.

This chapter will describe the anatomy of the eye and the visual performance that results from that structure combined with the information-processing capability of the brain. The ability of an observer to see an object depends on the object size, contrast, illumination, location of the object off the visual axis, exposure time, angular velocity between the object and the observer, amount of clutter in the scene, and perhaps other more subtle effects. The description of these dependencies is the most approximate part of the whole analysis of EO systems modeling; the human observer is simply the least understood component of the chain. Many models seem to gloss over this point, spending a great deal of effort in perfecting the system model, which of course adds little to the accuracy of the overall model if the human observer is only crudely modeled.

7.1 BASICS OF VISION

7.1.1 Anatomy of the Eye

The human eye is approximately spherical with a transparent bulge at the front surface; this is the cornea. Behind the cornea is the anterior chamber filled with a transparent fluid. Next is a structure of muscles and ligaments that support a flexible lens and an iris immediately in front of the lens. Behind the lens is a large chamber containing a clear liquid called the *vitreous humor*. Lining the rear hemisphere of the eyeball is the retina, which is a complex membrane that contains several layers of nerve cells through which light must pass before reaching the visual receptors, which are of two types, cones and rods. About 6° off the optical axis is a small area on the retina (about 1.5 mm in diameter) called the *fovea*. Within this area is a high density of cone receptors. In the very center of the fovea the cones are most densely packed, about 2 μm apart. This part of the retina forms the visual axis, along which visual acuity is a maximum. The density of cones decreases with distance from the visual axis.

Outside the fovea the rod receptors are located, increasing in density with distance from the fovea up to about 20° from the visual axis, beyond which their density decreases. The nerves from the cones and rods leave the retina as the optic nerve, located about 16° from the visual axis. The diameter of the optic nerve as it leaves the retina is about 2.5 mm. This discontinuity in the structure of the retina causes a blind spot, which, fortunately, is not apparent. A horizontal section through the right eye is shown in Figure 7.1. The distribution of the rods and cones, and the location of the blind spot are shown in Figure 7.2.

Light entering the eye passes through the iris, whose pupil adjusts between 2 and 7 mm, adapting to the ambient light level. It then passes through the lens, whose focal length is changed by the muscles attached to it. The focal length is adjusted to form a sharp image on the retina for objects anywhere from infinity to within a few inches of the eye, in a process called *accommodation*. The mosaic of cones and rods in the retina converts the retinal image into nerve impulses that are sent to the brain via the optic nerve. The cones provide color and detailed information, and function under relatively high levels of illumination; this is called *photopic vision*. In the fovea each cone has its own separate nerve path to the brain, which in part accounts for the high visual acuity in this part of the retina.

The rods are smaller than the cones and function at relatively low light levels, when the cones are inactive; this is called *scotopic vision*. Rods do not distinguish colors, and for that reason low light level scenes appear in shades of gray. Unlike the cones, several rods share the same ganglion cell that leads to the optic nerve. This is one reason why visual acuity is less with rods than with cones.

The distribution of cones and rods is the second factor that influences visual acuity. In the center of the fovea there are about 510 cones per mm. Two degrees off the visual axis the value has dropped to about 200 cones.

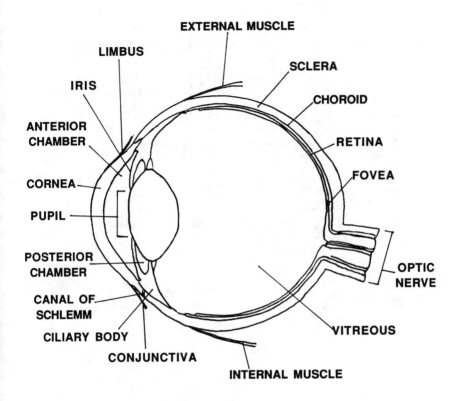

Figure 7.1 Horizontal cross section of the human right eye.

The spectral sensitivity of the cones is slightly different from that of the rods. Figure 7.3 shows the cones peaking at 555 nm and the rods at 510 nm. (Solar radiation peaks at about 555 nm. The radiation from the night sky has a slight shift toward shorter wavelengths.)

7.1.2 Foveal Vision

The distribution of the cones and rods and the separate ganglion connection of the cones to the optic nerve results in high visual acuity on the visual axis, decreasing to lower values toward the periphery of the field of view. Visual acuity is measured in terms of the smallest character that can be discerned. Most frequently used are uppercase letters and a heavy ring with a gap in the periphery. The letter E, for example, is composed of three horizontal bars and two spaces. Normal visual acuity is considered to be unity when the letter subtends five minutes of arc at the eye and each element subtends one minute. Visual acuity is the reciprocal of the angular

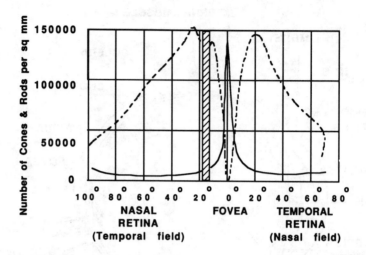

Figure 7.2 Distribution of rods and cones in the human eye.

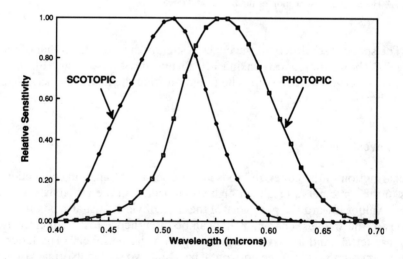

Figure 7.3 Spectral sensitivity of the human eye.

size (in minutes) of one of the elements of the letter that the observer can discern. The normal eye of a young person can resolve about one minute of arc (visual acuity of 1) under ordinary conditions. With adequate illumination the healthy unaided eye can resolve about 36 seconds of arc. A person who can resolve 40 seconds of arc has a visual acuity of 1.5.

Displacement of the target from the visual axis places the image on the retina in a region where the cones are less densely packed and the visual acuity is lower. Figure 7.4 shows that acuity decreases more rapidly with vertical image displacement from the fovea than with horizontal displacement.

The image of the world about us is stabilized on the retina by reflex movements of the eye evoked by stimulation of stretch receptors in the muscles of the head and neck and by hair cells in the vestibule of the ear. Additional eye movements enable us to perceive the world in sharp detail. The eyes are constantly in motion, even when a person is consciously trying to fixate on a given point. Involuntary eye movements are a high-frequency tremor, low-speed drift, and flicks—all of low amplitude. These small movements are apparently necessary for vision, for when the retinal image is artificially stabilized with a contact lens projector the conscious visual image fades out. It seems that the rods and cones become desensitized if the irradiance falling on them is absolutely unchanging.

In executing a visual search function, such as searching a battlefield for targets, the eye jumps from one fixation point to another, dwelling momentarily at each fixation. Each jump is called a *saccade*, after the French word for the flick of a sail, and has a certain amplitude. If the fixations are long and the saccades are

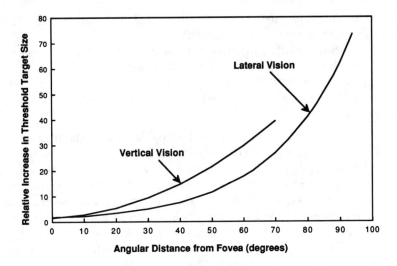

Figure 7.4 Variation of visual acuity with the angle off the fovea.

small, the time required to search a given sector will be excessive. If the saccades are large, the target may be missed. Experimental studies [1] have shown that both the average fixation time and the average saccadic size depend on the angular size of the search area presented to the observer. In general, if the search sector is larger, the observer makes larger jumps between fixations and dwells a shorter time at each. This behavior can be approximated by empirical power laws [2] for fixation or glimpse time and saccadic size:

$$t_g \approx .6836 \ \theta_S^{-0.2132} \tag{7.1}$$

$$s \approx .152 \ t_g^{-9.127} \tag{7.2}$$

where θ_S is the search sector in degrees. Actually the experimental data leading to (7.1) and (7.2) are for light to moderate clutter in the search sector. We also know that clutter affects the observer in the same direction as decreased search sector: one dwells longer at each fixation and makes smaller saccades. The fit of the empirical laws to the experimental results is shown in Figures 7.5 and 7.6.

7.2 ACQUISITION OF TARGETS

Detection, recognition, and identification of targets within a search sector are all included under the term *acquisition*. For our purposes we use the standard definitions of these levels of acquisition.

1. *Detection* means that the observer correctly indicates that an object of interest is in the field of view (e.g., a vehicle).
2. *Recognition* means that the observer correctly indicates the class to which the object belongs (e.g., a tank rather than a truck or APC).
3. *Identification* means that the observer correctly indicates the type or subclass of the object (e.g., a U.S. M1 tank rather than a Soviet T-72 or some other type).

It seems clear from these definitions that recognition and identification do not differ qualitatively: identification can be considered as recognition with a different (more specific) set of possible classes. In fact, some researchers [3] have also claimed that detection in clutter is a type of recognition with just two classes: object of interest and not an object of interest. On the other hand, it is possible to think of recognition and identification as special cases of detection by assuming that they involve detecting just smaller and smaller details within the detected target. This latter viewpoint is more or less the one adopted in the Air Standardization Agreement of 1976, setting minimum ground object sizes required in imagery for various levels of acquisition of various targets. There is now experimental evidence support-

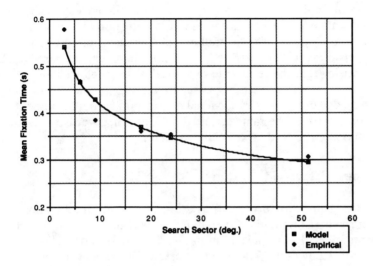

Figure 7.5 Average fixation time *versus* search sector.

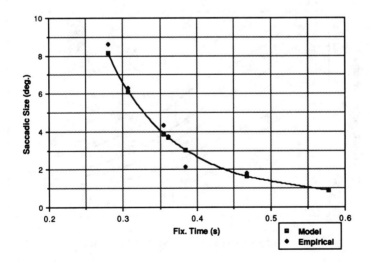

Figure 7.6 Average saccadic size *versus* fixation time.

ing this approach [4], showing that recognition of military vehicles through image intensifiers or thermal imagers is equivalent to detection of a smaller circular disc.

Usually the output of an overall model consists of the probabilities of these various levels of acquisition *versus* one or more independent variables. It should not be surprising that the results are expressed in terms of probabilities, as we are dealing ultimately with human responses to various stimuli. No two humans are exactly alike, and even a single individual may respond differently at different times to what appears to be the same set of stimuli. In other words, when dealing with human response, very little is absolutely certain.

7.2.1 Contrast Threshold

The detection capability of humans as a function of the three major variables of size, contrast, and brightness (or luminance) was determined in a classic set of experiments by H. R. Blackwell during World War II and published in 1946 [5]. This definitive study used 19 different observers (all young women) making a total of more than 200,000 observations of circular targets against uniform backgrounds, both light on dark and dark on light. The results were expressed in the form of contrast thresholds: the necessary contrast between target and background for 50% detection probability. In this experiment the observers had to make a small search in 6 seconds exposure time, as the target appeared randomly at one of eight major compass points, 3° off the initial central fixation point. The results are shown in Figure 7.7. As might be expected, threshold contrast decreases as either display

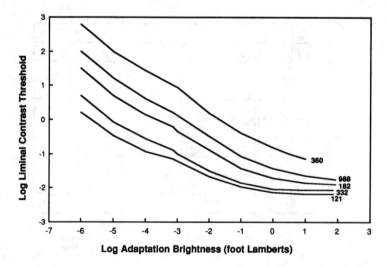

Figure 7.7 Threshold contrast *versus* adaptation brightness for five target sizes.

brightness or target size increases. However, one can see that all the curves flatten out at high brightness levels: the eye essentially saturates. Furthermore, at large target angular sizes, the change in threshold contrast with size also flattens out. The obvious inflection point in all the curves corresponds to a crossover the scotopic to photopic vision.

In later experiments [6], Blackwell and Taylor investigated shorter exposure times with the target appearing right on the fixation point. The curves of Figure 7.7 seem to also correctly describe the case of .33 second exposure with the target right on the visual axis.

The data on contrast thresholds are invaluable in constructing a model to predict human detection performance. They can be read directly from Blackwell's graphs or tables, however for computer models it is much more convenient to have equations. Purely empirical equations exist, along with others partially based on models of how the eye operates. Among the purely empirical equations we might note Koopman's particularly simple one [7]:

$$C_T A[1 - \exp(-\sqrt{K/A})^2] = R \tag{7.3}$$

where

$$C_T = \text{contrast threshold}$$
$$A = \text{target area in square minutes}$$
$$K, R = \text{constants in Table 7.1.}$$

Equation (7.3) quite nicely fits a wide range of data for .2 second exposure time. For luminances not contained in Table 7.1, presumably one could try some type of interpolation between the table values for K and R. Koopman also includes K

Table 7.1
Values of Koopman's Constants as
Functions of Background Luminance

$L(\text{fL})$	$R(\text{min}^2)$	$K(\text{min}^2)$
10^3	0.154	22
10^2	0.224	29
10^1	0.452	52
10^0	1.13	100
10^{-1}	4.03	160
10^{-2}	22.6	210
10^{-3}	190.0	270
10^{-4}	1860.0	330

and R values for one luminance (75 fL) in the .33 second exposure set of data mentioned previously: these turn out to be $R = 0.187$ min^2 and $K = 24$ min^2.

Another empirical approximation by Waldman, Wootton, and Hobson [8] allows continuous variation of luminance by using two formulas, one for the photopic region and one for the scotopic region (below about 7×10^{-4} fL). The results are, for photopic,

$$\log C_T = (.075 - 1.48 \times 10^{-4}\alpha)(\log L + 1.025 \log\alpha - 2.96)^2$$
$$- .601 \log\alpha - 1.04 \tag{7.4a}$$

for scotopic,

$$\log C_T = .1047(\log L + 1.991)^2 - 1.64 \log\alpha + 1.823 \tag{7.4b}$$

These equations fit the full range of Blackwell data for 6 seconds exposure, small search, or for .33 second exposure, no search.

A model of visual detection as the detection of differences between sensors across the target-background boundary in the presence of noise, led Overington [9] to formulas for foveal contrast threshold and even peripheral thresholds. These are too complex for presentation here, but the interested reader is referred to the original reference, which is well worth further study.

7.2.2 Johnson's Criteria

These studies mentioned previously could be described as approaches in the spatial domain. Another very famous approach uses the spatial frequency domain. It was designed specifically to treat the acquisition of targets by a human observer using an electronic imaging instrument. In 1958, Johnson [10] noted that the description of EO systems and components is significantly simpler in the frequency domain, because MTFs can be multiplied (assuming linear systems theory applies). The problem was that the targets used to establish MTF curves are simple three-bar or four-bar, black and white patterns that do not seem to have any straightforward relation to actual targets to be acquired in the field. Johnson claimed to have established that relationship: namely, that the number of lines in the bar target just resolvable across the minimum dimension of an actual target is roughly constant for any given level of acquisition. The idea is shown graphically in Figure 7.8. Table 7.2 shows the required resolvable lines required for the various tasks of detection, recognition, and identification.

Johnson's criteria as a basis for human modeling are open to a good deal of criticism. The first is that the work was never published in a peer-review journal,

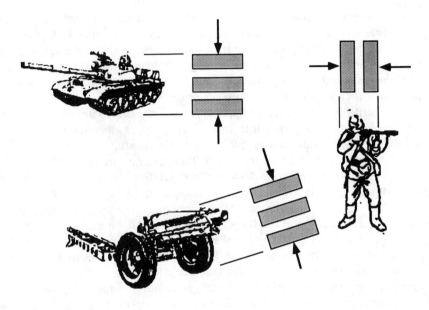

Figure 7.8 Equivalent bar targets for various field targets.

where the procedure could have been examined in detail. In fact, the paper itself [10] gives a very sketchy account of experimental procedure used in establishing the results; for example, no hint is given as to how the targets were presented to the observer or what times of observation were used. A better description is found in Rosell and Willson [11], although this of course is secondhand. These authors note that periodic patterns like those used to establish MTFs (or MRTDs for FLIRs) are more severely degraded by MTFs than are aperiodic real targets in the field, and therefore predictions based on Johnson's criteria are likely to be pessimistic.

Table 7.2
Johnson's Criteria

Discrimination Level	TV Lines per Minimum Object Dimension
Detection	$2^{+1.0}_{-0.5}$
Recognition	$8^{+1.6}_{-0.4}$
Identification	$12.8^{+3.2}_{-2.8}$

It might seem that Johnson's results imply that human acquisition depends solely on target size among the many image attributes, but Johnson himself was careful to note that the bar pattern contrast must be the same as the actual target contrast for his equivalent pattern results to apply. Despite this warning, MTFs or system resolution is still typically measured only with black-and-white bar patterns, with the results then applied with Johnson's criteria to field targets.

Another critic [4] notes that *recognition* is not well-defined in Johnson's work, because classification of a target into one of many types depends on the set of objects possible. The same author calls Johnson's criteria "ill-conceived" [12]. Although that critique may be a little harsh, there is one way in which Johnson's criterion for detection is self-contradictory. It states that, to detect a target (say, roughly rectangular) against some background, one must be able to resolve one line pair (a dark bar and a light bar with the same contrast as the real target) within the small angular dimension of the target, using the electro-optical system in question. But it is quite reasonable to regard resolution of the bar target as detection of one light bar surrounded by two dark bars [11], which implies that to detect a target of any size and contrast, one must detect a target of *half* the size and the same contrast! Now resolution of a bar target is not quite the same thing as detection of one bar between two others of different lightness, because just as the first has light smeared into it from the two surrounding bars, they themselves have the shade of the alternate bars smeared into them. However, this difference is just what was noted earlier by Rosell and Willson: any bar in a periodic target should be *harder* to detect than a single rectangle of the *same size as one bar* against a uniform background.

Another obvious weakness in Johnson's criteria is that they apply only to the situation where the observer is looking right at the target. There is no guidance in Johnson's work as to how to apply the detection criterion when the observer must search some significant area for the target. Obviously the latter situation is more common in practice than the former.

Despite all these criticisms, Johnson's criteria have been, and still are, very widely used, probably because they greatly facilitate the application of spatial frequency domain techniques to the problem of human target acquisition. It seems clear that they establish a relative difficulty scale between detection, recognition, and identification.

7.2.3 Display Signal-to-Noise Ratio

Still a separate approach emphasizes signal-to-noise ratio in the signal sent to the eye [11]. The basic supposition here is that each level of acquisition requires some threshold signal-to-noise ratio. In this view, Blackwell's results can be explained in terms of the signal-to-noise ratio inherent in the images presented, with the signal represented by contrast and the noise represented by photon noise. A very similar view is taken of Johnson's results, with the major difference being periodic targets instead of aperiodic ones.

Rosell and Willson combined analysis of SNR with a carefully thought out plan of psychophysical experiments to prove their point. Their presentation makes clear the conditions of the experiments, including observation time (10 seconds). In particular they analyzed a video system to derive what they name *display signal-to-noise ratio* (another author prefers the name *perceived signal-to-noise ratio* [13], because it does not exist in the display so much as in the observer's perception thereof) for an isolated rectangular target seen under conditions far from the resolution limit of the system:

$$\text{SNR}_{\text{DI}} = [2t\Delta f_v(a/A)]^{1/2} \text{SNR}_v \tag{7.5}$$

where

$$
\begin{aligned}
t &= \text{integration time of the eye} \\
\Delta f_v &= \text{video bandwidth} \\
a &= \text{area of target in the image} \\
A &= \text{area of field of view} \\
\text{SNR}_v &= \text{signal-to-noise ratio in video signal.}
\end{aligned}
$$

For a periodic bar target, they derived the expression

$$\text{SNR}_{\text{DI}} = (2t\Delta f_v/\alpha)^{1/2}(\epsilon/N)^{1/2}\text{SNR}_v \tag{7.6}$$

where

$$
\begin{aligned}
\alpha &= \text{displayed horizontal-to-vertical aspect ratio} \\
\epsilon &= \text{bar length-to-width ratio} \\
N &= \text{bar pattern spatial frequency (lines/picture height).}
\end{aligned}
$$

These expressions do not take into account system resolution (or MTF). The derivations presented to account for this factor seem to make many unsupported assumptions and eventually arrive at much more complicated equations than (7.5) and (7.6). Despite this, (7.5) and (7.6) were used to calculate SNR_{DI} for the first experiments, even though they were carried out with imagery presented on a CRT display. Perhaps the originators reasoned that the targets used were large enough that no system resolution questions needed consideration.

The detection experiments provided some gratifying results when rectangular targets were used: the threshold value (50% probability of detection) of SNR_{DI} was found to vary only slightly for a wide range of rectangular shapes and sizes.

For the most part, the value was close to 3. The same was true for a wide range of square target sizes. On the other hand, periodic bar targets showed a threshold SNR_{DI} that varied with both spatial frequency and height-to-width ratios of the patterns. Furthermore, as they began varying other parameters, such as display luminance, variations in threshold became more evident.

They also carried out experiments in recognition and identification of military vehicles, using the display signal-to-noise ratio concept. In these cases, values of SNR_{DI} were calculated using Johnson's equivalent bar pattern; in other words, for recognition, the formula for SNR_{DI} for a bar whose height was only 1/8 that of the vehicle was used. For recognition against a uniform background they obtained a threshold value of 3.3, whereas for natural scenery backgrounds the values ranged from 3.8 to 5.0, depending on the background. In identification experiments, threshold values ranged from 5.2 to 6.8.

Although Rosell and Willson have plausibility arguments to explain all the variability in their results, one must become rather discouraged when faced with the task of applying the display signal-to-noise ratio concept to prediction of system performance in the field. It would certainly be much more convincing if there had been less variation in threshold values over the different experimental conditions: the great variability suggests that the display signal-to-noise is not a very good general performance measure for acquisition modeling after all.

7.2.4 Search

When a search sector must be searched by an observer to find (detect) a target, the time required is obviously dependent on the dwell (or fixation) time and saccadic size. These are approximated by the empirical relations (7.1) and (7.2) of Section 7.1.2. However, for "quick and dirty" calculations, both quantities may be considered fixed, as in the *RCA Electro-Optics Handbook* [14]: $t_d \approx 0.3$ s and $s \approx 5°$. Then the time to completely search a sector α degrees by β degrees is

$$t_s = (\alpha/5)(\beta/5)0.3 \tag{7.7}$$

From Figures 7.6 and 7.7, we can see that these values are within a reasonable range for search sectors from 15° to 45°.

7.2.5 Motion

Any angular motion of the target with respect to the observer can have a marked effect on visual performance. However, the amount, and even the sense of the effect, depends on the task involved. For example, visual acuity drops with increasing target angular speed, but detection probability is enhanced (which should not be any surprise to hunters). Visual acuity tests always involve perception of some small detail in the test pattern, whereas detection just means the perception of some object of interest. Therefore, it is reasonable that a target should stand out and draw our attention if it is moving, even though the motion may make it difficult to discern details of the target. Experiments [15] have indicated that up to 5° per second, target detection enhancement can be described by a multiplier of the target contrast: in short, the effective contrast for detection of moving targets is

$$C_e = C(1 + 0.45 \, \omega^2) \tag{7.8}$$

where

C = actual contrast
ω = target angular speed in degrees/s.

7.3 ACQUISITION MODELS

7.3.1 Probability of Acquisition

The various thresholds discussed previously, such as Blackwell's contrast threshold, Johnson's required resolvable lines across the critical dimension, or Rosell and Willson's threshold signal-to-noise ratio, all refer to the 50% probability point of human performance. Now we expand our inquiry to seek methods for finding acquisition probabilities when we are not just at the threshold condition. Some type of ogive function in the normalized critical target variable is required. The value of the ogive curve is set to .5 when the normalized variable is unity, as shown in Figure 7.9. For example, when contrast is used, the normalized variable is called *contrast ratio*, CR ≡ actual contrast/threshold contrast.

Often the cumulative normal function is used for probability:

$$P = \phi[2.56(\text{CR} - 1)] \tag{7.9}$$

with

$$\phi(u) \equiv (2\pi)^{-.5} \int_{-\infty}^{u} \exp(-t^2/2) \, dt \tag{7.10}$$

A common analytic approximation to this function is

$$P_s \approx .5\{1 \pm \sqrt{1 - \exp[-4.2(\text{CR} - 1)^2]}\} \tag{7.11}$$

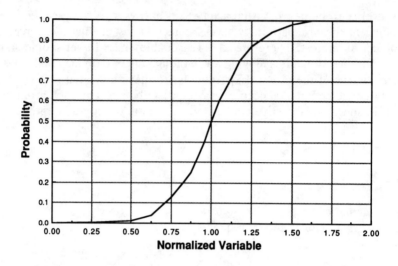

Figure 7.9 Example of the "probability of seeing" curve.

In (7.11), the positive sign is used for CR > 1 and the negative sign for CR < 1. Now it is a surprising fact that a much simpler function due to Seyb [16], with F_H = 1, approximates ϕ very nearly as well as (7.11) for values of CR > .5 (P_s values > .10):

$$P_s = 1 - 0.5^{(F_H CR)^3} \tag{7.12}$$

where F_H is the human factor (≥ 0 and ≤ 1).

Furthermore, (7.12) has some desirable properties that neither (7.10) nor (7.11) possesses. For lower values of contrast ratio, (7.12) gives smaller values for the probability than either of the others. In fact at CR = 0, (7.12) produces P = 0, whereas (7.10) and (7.11) give .005 and .004, respectively. Yet with uniform target and background, a displayed contrast of 0 should imply a target that is impossible to detect in principle; only (7.12) will produce this result. Also (7.12) incorporates the F_H factor, which Seyb tells us ranges from unity under laboratory conditions, down to values as low as .5 in the field. This additional variable allows the model to account for effects that can degrade human performance, such as fear, fatigue, boredom, or clutter. Note that F_H effectively raises the threshold contrast by just the factor $1/F_H$, which cc uld be done in any of the probability equations to account for differences betw en field and laboratory performance.

Search may be brought into the probability calculation in any one of several ways. A "detection lobe" theory makes the probability of detection a function of target angle off the visual axis. That is, contrast threshold may be expressed as a monotonically decreasing function of this angle [8], and then probability is calculated with equations like (7.10) through (7.12). On the other hand, probability may be taken as a binary variable with respect to angle off-axis: a nonzero value for some small area around the visual axis (often taken as the nominal angular size of the fovea), and 0 for any greater angle. Then it is usual to multiply by a probability that the observer has fixated so that the target is within the critical area (the probability that the observer "looks at" the target in the allotted search time).

7.3.2 Early Models

Drawing primarily upon the work of Blackwell and Johnson and the new computing power, many of the major players in the defense industry attempted to build acquisition models in the late 1960s. These, of necessity, included human acquisition submodels.

7.3.2.1 MARSAM

Perhaps the most notable of these early efforts was Honeywell's *Multiple Airborne Reconnaissance Sensor Assessment Model* (MARSAM), which allowed analysis of TV, FLIR, or MTI radar systems. The same human submodel was applied to the display of each of these. This submodel is one of a group that could be called *separable variable models*.

Detection probability, P_d, was calculated as a product of other probabilities, described as

1. P_{d1}^*, probability that target-element size and contrast in display are sufficient for detection.
2. P_{d2}^*, probability that a displayed element will be fixated on by the observer within a specified time.
3. P_{d3}^*, probability that an observer-viewed element will be correctly discriminated from confusing objects.
4. P_{d4}^*, probability of sufficient signal-to-noise ratio for detection.
5. P_{LOS}, probability that a line of sight exists between the target and the sensor.

Only P_{d2}^* and P_{d3}^* were considered interdependent, whereas all the others were considered independent probabilities. Therefore, the overall probability of detection was written as

$$P_d = P_{LOS} P_{d1}^* P_{d2}^* (P_{d3}^*) P_{d4}^* \tag{7.13}$$

The algorithm for recognition probability, P_r, introduced another probability (assumed independent): P_r^*, the probability that system resolution is sufficient to allow recognition, given that detection has occurred. Then,

$$P_r = P_d P_r^* \tag{7.14}$$

We shall return to the question of the validity of (7.13) and (7.14), but first we shall examine the algorithms for the individual probabilities.

The algorithm used for P_{d1}^* is the familiar one of (7.11), with an approximate expression for contrast threshold, C_T, that fits Blackwell's data for a light level of 10 fL. This light level presumably was considered typical for displays, and C_T is not very sensitive to this variable at higher light levels anyway.

The probability P_{d2}^* was written in terms of P_{d3}^* as

$$P_{d2}^* = 1 - [1 - P_{d3}^*(A_e/A_d)]^n \tag{7.15}$$

with

$$n = t/t_g \tag{7.16}$$

where

A_e = area searched by eye in one glance
A_d = display area (same units as A_e)
t = total search time
t_g = average time for one glimpse or fixation
n = number of fixations in the whole search time.

This formulation is essentially that of the probability of detection in a random search of the display, when the detection probability in a single fixation is $P_{d3}^*(A_e/A_d)$. For the convenience of computation, (7.15) was approximated by

$$P_{d2}^* \approx 1 - \exp[-P_{d3}^*(A_e/A_d)(t/t_g)] \tag{7.17}$$

and A_e was taken as $5°$, t_g as $.3\ s$, just as in Section 7.2.4.

Clutter enters into the calculation of P_{d3}^*. An empirical fit to much earlier studies by Boynton was used:

$$P_{d3}^* = \left[1 + \left(\frac{M}{29\, t_g^{0.93}}\right)^{1.29}\right]^{-1} \tag{7.18}$$

where M is the number of confusing objects in A_e.

Similarly, an empirical fit to work by Schade was used for P_{d4}^*:

$$P_{d4}^* \approx 1 - \exp(-0.45\, \text{SNR}^{1/37}) \tag{7.19}$$

where SNR is the signal-to-noise ratio in the display.

For recognition, a Johnson's type criterion is invoked:

$$P_r^* = \begin{cases} 1 - \exp[-(N - 3.2)^2], & N > 3.2 \\ 0, & N \le 3.2 \end{cases} \tag{7.20}$$

where N is the resolvable lines across minimum target dimension. This algorithm gives a 50% probability when $N \approx 6$.

In evaluating such a comprehensive model, we first note that (7.13) implies a separability of most of the relevant variables, which is most doubtful. Insofar as the probabilities are those for independent events or are conditional probabilities, the simple multiplication is legitimate. But a close analysis shows that the word definitions of the probabilities are distorted in such a way as to make them seem like conditional probabilities that may be multiplied, whereas the actual algorithms for the same probabilities belie the definitions. For example P_{d1}^* is supposed to be the probability that the target size and contrast are sufficient for detection, and if that were true then it would be independent of the others. But for the definition to be literally true, we would have to have the situation where probability of detection is a step function of size and contrast (0 below some critical values of the variables and unity above), and P_{d1}^* would be the probability of occurrence of target size and contrast above the critical values (a probability clearly independent of any clutter or SNR values). Of course, that is not at all what is calculated by (7.11). Rather P_{d1}^* as calculated is the probability of detection, *given that the size and contrast have certain values and that clutter is absent and SNR is high*. Actually the probability of detection in a single glimpse, as used in the formulation of P_{d2}^* is a function of size, contrast, light level, clutter, and so forth. There is really no evidence that justifies the separability of variables into a product form. How all the variables should be included in a formulation for P_{d2}^* is shown more correctly in Section 7.3.4.

7.3.2.2 SRI LLLTV Model

Another model of the same era (circa 1968) was *Stanford Research Institute's* (SRI) *low-light-level TV* (LLLTV) model. The human submodel here was much simpler and set the tone for many later models. Human acquisition was based solely on Johnson's criteria. The received contrast (or modulation) and faceplate illumination selected an operating resolution for the system, and with that resolution, the number of resolvable lines across the target could be calculated and used with Johnson's criteria to give acquisition probabilities.

7.3.2.3 Bailey-Rand Model

A more rigorous attempt to build a human acquisition model, including search and clutter, was undertaken in 1970 by H. H. Bailey at the Rand Corporation [17]. The investigator, realistically noting the heuristic nature of the model and the difficulty of precisely specifying the input values, warns that the model should be used only in estimating bounds to human performance.

The model considers target detection as recognition in the presence of clutter and then expresses the final probability of recognizing the target as a product of four factors, more carefully defined than in MARSAM:

1. P_1, probability that the observer makes a fixation on the target during the search.
2. P_2, probability of detection of the target if it is viewed foveally, without noise.
3. P_3 probability that the target is recognized, given that it is detected.
4. η, noise degradation factor.

Because P_2 and P_3 represent probabilities conditional on the occurrence of the previous event, the overall probability of target recognition is written

$$P_R = P_1 P_2 P_3 \eta \qquad (7.21)$$

For the first factor, which includes all search assumptions, Bailey heuristically derives an expression for random search with a fixed "glimpse aperture" and fixed fixation time of .333 s, which is very reminiscent of the MARSAM term P_{d3}^*.

$$P_1 = 1 - \exp[-(700/G)(a_T/A_S)t] \qquad (7.22)$$

where

G = average number of fixation centers per glimpse aperture
a_T = area of target

A_S = area of search (same units as a_T)
t = time in seconds.

The fixed glimpse aperture essentially means that there is a single detection probability if the target is within the glimpse aperture, and 0 probability otherwise. Neither this assumption nor the single fixation time is strictly true. G is the variable that expresses scene clutter, because fixation centers are those nontarget objects within the scene that are enough like the target to attract fixations. Obviously, the value of G can be estimated in only the crudest of manners (Bailey suggests values between 1 and 10 for most searches of interest). Despite these drawbacks, the model is to be commended for including the important variables of time, search sector, and clutter.

The probability of detection factor, P_2, is based on Blackwell's data, with a multiplier on the threshold contrast to account for field rather than laboratory conditions. Furthermore, Bailey removes luminance level as a variable by assuming photopic vision at high light level: 30 to 100 fL. The applicable threshold contrast is approximated by

$$(\log C_T + 2)(\log \alpha + 0.5) = 1 \tag{7.23}$$

where α is the target angular size in minutes. Once a threshold contrast is established, detection probability, P_2, follows from the previously mentioned (7.10) through (7.11).

Probability of recognition, given prior detection, was calculated in the spirit of Johnson's criteria: determined by the number of resolvable spots, N_r, across the minimum dimension of the target. The formula adopted was

$$P_3 = \begin{cases} 1 - \exp\{-[(N_r/2) - 1]^2\}, & N_r \geq 2 \\ 0, & N_r < 2 \end{cases} \tag{7.24}$$

This expression implies $P_3 \approx 0.9$ when $N_r = 5$.

The noise term is the most problematical of all and receives little discussion in the documentation. It seems questionable that all the effects of a noisy image can be accurately modeled by a single multiplicative factor. Just as in MARSAM, the modeler is making an unjustified assumption of separability of variables. In both models it seems legitimate to question not just the separability of the SNR contribution, but also whether a noisy image is not *perceptually* the same thing as reduced contrast, in which case it should be included within the P_2 term somehow. Nevertheless, a few brief arguments led Bailey to the equation

$$\eta = \begin{cases} 1 - \exp[-(\mathrm{SNR} - 1)], & \mathrm{SNR} \geq 1 \\ 0, & \mathrm{SNR} < 1 \end{cases} \tag{7.25}$$

Although the Bailey-Rand model is a very early attempt at a complete visual acquisition model and certainly has its deficiencies, in many ways it is a very astute effort, particularly in its attempt to include all of the most important variables and in the exemplarily candid documentation.

7.3.3 C2NVEO Models

The U.S. Army CECOM center for *Night Vision and Electro-Optics* (C2NVEO) has produced several end-to-end acquisition models that have been widely used within the U.S. defense industry. These include the 1975 static performance model for thermal viewing systems (also widely known as the *Ratches model*), the 1985 image intensifier performance model, and the 1990 thermal imaging systems performance model (also known as FLIR90). The first and the last of these model human acquisition with thermal imaging systems, and the other models human acquisition with image intensifiers, direct view optics, or the unaided eye. All three have human submodels based exclusively on Johnson's criteria and are basically static models: the observer is assumed to be looking at the target position and is allowed unlimited time. Essentially, the acquisition problem is reduced to simply finding the number of resolvable cycles across the minimum dimension of the target seen through the imaging system; all acquisition probabilities follow from that variable.

The visual acquisition model [18] works with something called *minimum resolvable contrast* (MRC), which is a function of spatial frequency and light level. One such function is specified for the eye, and another is given for image intensifier systems. Very little justification is given for the specific forms used, and the serious student can only be frustrated by extensive references to unpublished, undated, internal reports in the documentation. It is claimed that the unaided eye function is validated by Blackwell, and reference is made to his original 1946 paper, however this claim is hard to take seriously as Blackwell's work is all in the spatial, not the spatial frequency, domain, and it is exactly the pertinence of these two different domains to human performance that is the crucial question. Nevertheless, the model proceeds by taking the displayed contrast as the MRC to calculate maximum resolvable frequency. From maximum resolvable frequency and target size, the number of resolvable cycles across the target is determined; and from resolvable cycles, acquisition probability follows "through an empirically established set of functions called *target transfer probability functions* (TTPF)." These latter functions (whose sole explanation is contained in the quoted phrase) are reasonably shaped ogive curves with Johnson's criteria at the 50% points. They are tabulated in Table 7.3.

Table 7.3
C2NVEO Target Transfer Probability Functions

| Probability | Number of Resolvable Cycles across Target | | |
	Detection	Recognition	Identification
1.0	1.5–3	9–12	18–24
.95	1.2	6–12	12–16
.80	.75–1.5	4.5–6	9–12
.50	.5–1	3–4	6–8
.30	.375–.75	2.25–3	4.5–6
.10	.25–.5	1.5–2	3–4
.02	.125–.25	.75–1	1.5–2

The two thermal imaging systems models have human submodels very similar to that just described, with the one difference that the MRTD replaces the MRC. The major weakness in all the C2NVEOL models is their rather inbred nature and total reliance on Johnson's criteria. In fact, the human submodels of all these programs offer little improvement over the simple SRI model of 1968. Also they are all static models (no search), except that ACQUIRE, the submodel of FLIR90 that contains the human performance, does allow the user to enter a search time that prompts the program to perform some sort of search calculation. This search algorithm is not well documented, but probably consists of a multiplication by a "probability of looking at" as described in Section 7.3.1. However, one is not encouraged to place much faith in this search calculation because no entry of search sector is required, and it is difficult to believe that probability of detection within some given search time is independent of how much angular area must be searched. Their strengths are primarily in their sophisticated system characterization (to be discussed in Chapter 8) and in the fact that they have served as standards, which allow the comparison of the performance of different systems on a consistent basis.

7.3.4 Spatial Domain Empirical Model

It is possible to build a human acquisition with search in a clutter model [8], based almost exclusively on empirical relationships that have been established in experiments. Considering search as a random set of fixations within some search sector, the cumulative detection probability is

$$P_d = 1 - (1 - P_g)^n \tag{7.26}$$

with

$$n = (t - t_r)/t_g \tag{7.27}$$

where

P_g = average detection probability in one fixation
t = total time of search
t_r = reaction time
t_g = average fixation or glimpse time
N = number of fixations in the whole search.

Often, for the search times of interest, t_r is negligible (only a few tenths of a second).

The model finds P_g as an average over all the fixation positions within the search, using the saccadic size as given by (7.2) and the glimpse time as given by (7.1). The target is assumed to be at the center of the search sector and all fixation positions are assumed to be equally likely. Then the probability for each fixation position is calculated from Seyb's algorithm, (7.12), using (7.4) for foveal threshold contrast and an additional empirical relation for a parafoveal threshold. The inclusion of a parafoveal contrast threshold means that off-axis detection is included in this approach, which qualifies as a type of "detection lobe" theory. Empirical formulas may also be used to adjust the human factor, F_H, for clutter.

The advantage of this approach is that all the fundamental variables of search, clutter, and time are specifically taken into account in a manner firmly based on experimental evidence. However there is much room for error in applying laboratory results to field predictions, and the human factor, F_H, is the parameter we have to adjust for this. As noted earlier, this factor in effect raises the contrast threshold.

REFERENCES

1. J.M. Enoch, "Effect of the Size of a Complex Display upon Visual Search," *J. Opt. Soc. Am.*, Vol. 49, 1959, pp. 280–286.
2. G. Waldman, J. Wootton, G. Hobson, and K. Luetkemeyer, "A Normalized Clutter Measure for Images," *Comp. Vis., Graphics, and Image Proc.*, Vol. 42, 1988, pp. 137–156.
3. J.A. Ratches *et al.*, "Night Vision Laboratory Static Performance Model for Thermal Viewing Systems," U.S. Army Electronics Command, Night Vision Laboratory, April 1975.
4. A. van Meeteren, "Characterization of Task Performance with Viewing Instruments," *J. Opt. Soc. Am.*, Vol. A7, 1990, pp. 2016–2023.
5. H.R. Blackwell, "Contrast Thresholds of the Human Eye," *J. Opt. Soc. Am.*, Vol. 36, 1946, pp. 624–643.

6.   H.R. Blackwell and J.R. Taylor, "Survey of Laboratory Studies of Visual Detection," NATO Seminar on Detection, Recognition, and Identification of Line of Sight Targets, The Hague, Netherlands, 1969.
7.   B.O. Koopman, "An Empirical Formula for Visual Search," *Oper. Res.*, Vol. 33, 1986, pp. 377–383.
8.   G. Waldman, J. Wootton, and G. Hobson, "Visual Detection with Search: An Empirical Model," *IEEE Trans. on Systems, Man, & Cyber.*, Vol. 21, 1991, pp. 596–606.
9.   I. Overington, "Interaction of Vision with Optical Aids," *J. Opt. Soc. Am.*, Vol. 63, 1973, pp. 1043–1049.
10. J. Johnson, "Analysis of Image Forming Systems," presented at Image Intensifier Symposium, Fort Belvoir, VA, October 1958.
11. F.A. Rosell and R.H. Willson, "Recent Psychophysical Experiments and the Display Signal-to-Noise Ratio Concept," in *Perception of Displayed Information*, ed. L. Biberman, Plenum Press, New York, 1973.
12. J.J. Vos and A. van Meeteren, "PHIND: An Analytical Model to Predict Target Acquisition Distance with Image Intensifiers," *Appl. Opt.*, Vol. 30, March 10, 1991, pp. 958–966.
13. J.M. Lloyd, *Thermal Imaging Systems*, Plenum Press, New York, 1975, p. 144.
14. *RCA Electro-Optics Handbook*, Tech. Series EOH-11, RCA Solid State Division, 1974, p. 121.
15. H.E. Petersen and D.J. Dugas, "The Relative Importance of Contrast and Motion in Visual Detection," *Human Factors*, Vol. 14, 1972, pp. 207–216.
16. E.K. Seyb, "Influence of Search Mode on Visual Detection of Airborne Targets," SHAPE Tech. Memo STC TM-458, 1975.
17. H.H. Bailey, "Target Detection Through Visual Recognition," Rand Corp. Memor. RM6158/1-PR, February 1970, p. 13.
18. J.A. Leslie *et al.*, "Reference and User's Manual for NV&EOL, Visionics Division Image Intensifier Performance Model," Dept. of the Army, Night Vision and Electro-Optics Center, Visionics Div., Fort Belvoir, VA, April 1985.

Chapter 8
End-to-End Models

8.1 INTRODUCTION AND OVERVIEW

This chapter is a natural conclusion to this book. The individual chapters have sequentially inspected and analyzed the required elements of an end-to-end model as outlined in Figure 8.1. The reader is now armed with the ability to put it all together in one end-to-end model. You should have sufficient knowledge of the subject matter to know the limitations of the end model in regard to the underlying assumptions of the individual elements chosen for the model. In this chapter we look at various investigators' attempts to construct overall models that address the issue of target acquisition performance of various electro-optical systems.

Here we would like to reflect the thoughts of Chapter 1 as regards the philosophy of modeling. Models need to be balanced according to the significance of any of the elements given in Figure 8.1 to the purpose of the model. This avoids including parts of the model that are overly complex, "calculated to the fifth decimal place," when the overall accuracy of the model would be unchanged if the calculation were to the "first decimal place." All models are in some way an approximation of reality. The significance of the degree to which the result differs from reality depends on the purpose of the model. Often models are criticized because they have been used beyond the purpose for which they were intended. The criticism should not be of the model but of the analyst who used it for a task for which it was unsuitable.

In this chapter we focus on end-to-end models developed by various researchers. Our discussion will focus on the ability of the models for the tasks intended and possible extensions beyond the original intent. We will delineate for each model whether it was intended for use in the visual or the IR band, whether it is analytical in nature or produces synthetic imagery, whether it is simplistic or detailed, and whether it deals with the spatial domain or the spatial-frequency domain. We will discuss each model's strengths and weaknesses.

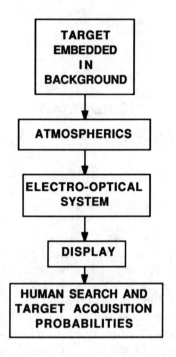

Figure 8.1 Elements of electro-optical systems modeling.

We have chosen 12 from the many models available for discussion. Starting with some pre-1975 models through to two models developed by us, one covering the infrared band and the other covering the visual band. The total list of models chosen for review are as given in Table 8.1. In the description of the individual models we have used the nomenclature of the original authors to avoid confusion to the reader who further researches these works. Where unfamiliar nomenclature is used we have attempted to clarify it so that this book can stand alone as a reference.

8.2 MODELS TO 1975

8.2.1 SRI LLLTV Model

The SRI LLLTV model [1] is a very simple end-to-end model, designed to calculate acquisition probabilities for an airborne, low-light-level TV system looking downward laterally from the flight path. Despite the motion implied, no explicit account

Table 8.1
Model List

Pre-1975:
 SRI LLLTV
 MARSAM FLIR
 Bailey-Rand
 GAVID

NVL Suite:
 NVL Static Performance
 Image Intensifier Performance
 FLIR90

Other Contemporary:
 VOM
 TTIM
 PHIND
 VISDET
 IRDET

is taken of motion effects (e.g., image motion MTF, limited target time in FOV, reduction of human visual acuity with image motion). This lack of consideration of motion is consistent with the overall simplicity of the model. In that respect, the model is admirably consistent in the level with which it treats all aspects of the problem. It is described here, using the original notation as much as is practical.

Geometric inputs are aircraft altitude, H, and lateral ground distance of target from flight path, Y. These are combined within the program to produce slant range S_r:

$$S_r = \sqrt{Y^2 + H^2} \tag{8.1}$$

The target and background inputs are only background reflectance, R_b, target reflectance, R_t, target width, W_t, and target height, H_t. The reflectances are combined to give target contrast, defined in this model as just the ratio

$$C_t = R_t/R_b \tag{8.2}$$

This ratio is what we would prefer to call inherent contrast plus unity. It should also be noted that the SRI model does allow for the ratio to be the inverse of that shown in (8.2), if the background reflectance is higher. Target dimensions are multiplied together later in the algorithm, when resolvable elements on target are needed.

Environmental input consists of the scene illuminance, I_s, visibility range, V_r, and atmospheric transmission coefficient, τ_a. The inclusion of both visibility and atmospheric transmittance is a rather curious quirk of this model, because, to the accuracy modeled, one could be calculated from the other (see for example, (5.20) in Chapter 5). The visibility range is used in a contrast reduction algorithm very much like that of Chapter 5, (5.23) for a target against a terrain background, but also with the inclusion of (5.34) for the scattering coefficient to allow for the sensor spectral response to differ from that of the eye. The only problem is that the SRI algorithm appears to mistake the sky-ground ratio of Chapter 5 with the ratio of (8.2). The resulting apparent target contrast, C_a, (reduced by the atmosphere) is used to calculate the apparent contrast modulation:

$$M_a = \frac{C_a - 1}{C_a + 1} \tag{8.3}$$

System inputs required are photocathode midresponse wavelength, λ_{pc}, optics focal length, f, optics F-number, $f\#$, optics transmission, τ_l, and maximum possible system resolution in TV lines per picture height, N'_{max}. The first system calculation is to find the photocathode illuminance by

$$I_{pc} = \frac{\tau_a \tau_l R_t I_s}{4f\#^2} \tag{8.4}$$

The perspicacious reader might recognize (8.4) as the combination of earlier equations in this book; namely, (6.48), (5.8), and (4.3). We should perhaps note that (5.8), and therefore (8.4) also, ignores any atmospheric in-scattering. The rest of the system calculations uses empirical approximations that are specific to one assumed TV system; simulation of a different system would require the insertion of a different set of empirical approximations. The faceplate illuminance is used in one instance to determine the limiting resolution, N_{max}, from an empirical curve expressing limiting resolution as a function of faceplate illumination and N'_{max}. However, the model builders correctly recognized that such TV-system-limiting resolution curves are determined with 100% modulation (black and white) bar targets, whereas the apparent modulation of the target is likely to be significantly less. Therefore I_{pc} is also used with M_a and N_{max} in another empirical relationship to calculate the operating resolution of the system, N, for the actual modulation of the target to be acquired. Thus it seems that N'_{max}, N_{max}, and N represent the system limiting resolution with a 100% target modulation and very high photocathode illuminance, with a 100% target modulation and actual photocathode illuminance, and with the actual target modulation and actual photocathode illuminance, respectively. No allowance is made for separating the effects of the different components of the system (optics, TV tube, display). Once the operating resolution of the system is established and a specific photocathode size is assumed, it is straightforward to calculate the resolution element (assumed square) size, D_t, at the target distance. Finally, the number of elements resolved within the target is calculated:

$$N_t = W_t H_t / D_t^2 \tag{8.5}$$

The only input pertaining to the human observer is "viewer efficiency," P_v, which is a factor that directly multiplies the probability of detection. Not even viewer distance from the display is required, although it is obvious that that distance is an important variable in human acquisition. As described in the previous chapter, the human observer submodel is a simple Johnson's criterion type calculation, with conditional detection probability, P_d^*, dependent only on resolved elements, N_t, in an empirical relationship. This probability is conditional on the existence of a line of sight and is multiplied by a separate line-of-sight probability, P_{LOS}, and the viewer efficiency, P_v, to arrive at the final detection probability:

$$P_d = P_d^* P_{LOS} P_v \tag{8.6}$$

Both recognition probability and identification probability are also calculated, and they are also dependent only on N_t.

The SRI LLLTV model is a good example of an early, basic end-to-end model. It is consistent in its level of treatment of all aspects of the acquisition problem. Of course, it is oversimplified in its target and background, atmospheric, and human submodels, but such simplification is legitimate as long as the user is aware of it. The main drawback would seem to be the way in which the system and its geometry are hardwired into the model. Simulation of a different system or the replacement of some system component would require much work on the part of the user. Also, the model can simulate only the static (no search) case of an airborne sensor viewing a ground target against a terrain background.

8.2.2 MARSAM FLIR Model

As mentioned in the previous chapter, MARSAM was a very ambitious program to simulate several types of airborne sensors. As an example of an early, but more complex model, we describe the FLIR portion briefly here. This FLIR model consists of five, fairly complicated submodels before the human factors submodel (described in Chapter 7) is entered. These five are

1. Sensor-to-target element geometry submodel
2. Multiple background and element resolvability geometry submodel

3. Atmospheric effects submodel
4. Receiver power output submodel
5. Display submodel.

As in the SRI LLLTV model, MARSAM considers only the case of the sensor on an airborne platform, moving horizontally and looking downward at some depression angle perpendicular to the line of flight. The first calculations in the sensor-to-target geometry submodel look very similar to the SRI model: with the input of altitude, H, and depression angle, ϕ, the slant range S_r is calculated

$$S_r = H/\sin\phi \tag{8.7}$$

Also the input target dimensions D_{tx} and D_{ty} are multiplied to get target element area. This submodel also requires the input of system angular resolution in the in-flight and cross-track directions, $\Delta\theta_x$ and $\Delta\theta_y$, similar to what we would today call instantaneous field of view. These are used with S_r to calculate ground-resolved distances in the two orthogonal directions, D_{gx} and D_{gy}:

$$D_{gx} = \Delta\theta_x S_r^2/H \tag{8.8a}$$

$$D_{gy} = \Delta\theta_y S_r \tag{8.8b}$$

These two quantities multiplied together give a ground-resolved area that is then divided into the target area to arrive at the number of ground-resolved areas on a target element. The rest of this geometry submodel and the second geometry submodel concern questions of background and target within one resolution element, multiple background types, and multiple targets. They become rather involved and need not concern us here, for they are outside the scope of this book.

The atmospherics of MARSAM are similar to the empirical IR method of Section 5.2.3, in that scattering and absorption transmissions are computed separately and then multiplied to get an overall loss factor. As in that algorithm, MARSAM requires the input of air temperature and relative humidity and the wavelength band of interest. One difference is that absorption due to both water and carbon dioxide is computed in MARSAM. The scattering transmission is calculated primarily from visibility.

The receiver power output submodel of MARSAM is rather unique in its approach. It uses the previously calculated ground-resolved and target areas, slant range, and atmospheric transmission along with input values for background temperature, target temperature difference, emissivities, and wavelength band to calculate the power received from both a background resolution cell and the resolution cell containing the target (which may also contain some background, as determined by the geometry submodels). Also the system *noise equivalent power* (NEP) is calculated from system inputs, including NETD. The received target and background powers are then both modified by the system's linear or lin-log response curve (user choice), and for each, the maximum of either the modified power or the NEP is passed on to the display submodel.

In the display submodel, a signal-to-noise ratio is immediately calculated from the target and background powers and the NEP; SNR passes directly to the human submodel to be used in the computation of P_{d4}^*, as described in Section 7.3.2. Also the time in view is calculated for the case of a moving display, although a stationary display (freeze frame) is allowed too. However, the major part of this submodel is concerned with calculation of geometrical scale factors to get the target displayed size and voltage scale factors to be used in obtaining displayed contrast. That is, MARSAM rather ambitiously tries to model the display in detail by considering the actual signal voltages and the display transfer characteristics to derive actual displayed luminances for target and background. This approach is rigorous but difficult and requires some rather detailed knowledge of the display system. Sent to the human factors submodel (besides SNR) are time in view, target element dimension on display, displayed contrast, and number of resolution elements on target.

MARSAM was admirably ambitious and advanced for its time period. It was built before the time of LOWTRAN, and obviously could have profited much from that atmospheric model, as its own atmospherics are rather weak compared to the level of the rest of the model. In its sensor and display submodels it is unusually rigorous, but this same rigor requires the user to enter detailed system information, which is often difficult to obtain. These submodels could have profited from the more modern approach of using system summary performance measures, at least to some extent. The human submodel of MARSAM has been criticized in Chapter 7.

8.2.3 Bailey-Rand Model

The Bailey-Rand model, sponsored by the U.S. Air Force, is a target recognition model produced in the late 1960s [2]. Considering the time frame in which it originated, it is a remarkable piece of research. Bailey's memorandum covering the model development is clear and well referenced. He describes in detail the methodology chosen and its theoretical or, as was more often the case, its empirical basis. Any criticism of the model using a 1990 perspective should be tempered by consideration of the state of the art of the era of its conception. Bailey provides valuable insights not only to his model but to all models that attempt to mathematically describe the target detection process involving the vagaries and variances of the human being. In reflection of its sponsorship, the model is tailored to the case of the airborne observer but may be extended to other situations.

Bailey constrains the applicability of the model to situations of active search in a structured field for known (or prebriefed) specific objects. Such cases, as are pointed out by the author, minimize the dominant sources of variability and unpredictability in human behavior. By such constraints the subjective act of human behavior can be constrained to give reproducible results. His comments are well founded in that all models imply the presence of a target and that the search is for a fairly short period of time under conditions of strong motivation.

Bailey proposes a straightforward model for overall probability of target recognition, as described by (7.21) in Section 7.3.2. Equation (7.22) describes P_1 as representing the search term probability; P_2, as described by (7.11), is the contrast term in accord with Blackwell's results; P_3, as described by (7.24), is the resolution term in line with Johnson's work; and η, as described by (7.25), represents degradation of the three prior terms due to display noise. The model has the attributes of recognizing that the process of predicting the probability of detection is driven by search, size, contrast, clutter, and display noise.

The first term deals with the element of search. Bailey consciously ignores the visual lobe theory of search, ignores off-axis detections, ignores moving targets and motion cues, and bases his search on foveal vision. He recognizes that the eye moves in discrete steps called *fixations*, and his model assumes that these are of constant fixation time of 0.33 seconds. The model assumes that an observer moves an apparent aperture (his foveal lobe) regularly over the area of interest. The observer is assumed to adjust the average interfixation distance in accordance with an *a priori* expectation of target size and contrast. There is some evidence that this phenomena occurs in reality; that is, that observers change their saccadic intervals and search patterns according to what is being searched for. Bailey introduces the concept of the effective scanning aperture, called a *glimpse aperture*, A_g, which is the area for which foveal detection is effective. A_g is nominally between 10 to 100 times the target area. The scanning aperture is also adjusted to accommodate a measure of scene clutter. Clutter according to Bailey is addressed by a vague notion of scene "congestion," or other "confusing objects" that are present in the scene. There is no mathematical formulation of scene clutter.

The basis for the second term in the Bailey-Rand model is Blackwell's contrast threshold data for glimpses of 0.33 seconds with 30 to 100 fL average scene brightness. Bailey modifies this threshold to accommodate various "field factors"; these include vibrational factors and dynamic range, and in essence, degrade Blackwell's threshold by a factor of 5.5 in contrast.

The third term, designated the resolution term, P_3, relies heavily on Johnson's criteria for the minimum target dimension. A simple parameter, N_R, is used as the number of resolution cells contained in the shortest dimension across a target. *Resolution cells* here mean independently detectable spots at the contrast of the target. The procedure for determining this value is to ascertain the contrast of the target. At this contrast level, the spot size that would yield a 90% probability of detection is deemed the size of independent detectable spots. This size, divided into the target minimum dimension, yields the number of resolvable spots, N_R.

The last term in the model, η, attempts to accommodate displayed noise. Noise, Bailey claims, increases scene "congestion" and therefore reduces P_1; increases threshold contrast, C_T, and therefore reduces P_2; and increases the required value of N_R and so reduces P_3. He lumps all three effects into a single degradation factor called η.

By substituting (7.22), (7.11), (7.24), and (7.25) into equation (7.21), Bailey produced an overall simple model that could be driven with very few inputs. For unaided vision and pure optical systems all we require are the variables on the left-hand side of Table 8.2. For detection using a TV, radar, or FLIR we require the variables on the right-hand side of Table 8.2. The model is straightforward to use, but the user is still left with considerable off-line calculations to provide the necessary parameters, in particular the observed contrast.

Table 8.2
Parameters Required for Bailey-Rand Model

Unaided Eye or Optical System	Sensor System
Apparent size	Displayed contrast
Target contrast	Scale
Desired search rate	Resolution
Congestion	Noise

A few final comments are deemed necessary before we close this section on the Bailey-Rand model. The model does have several weaknesses. These revolve around principally the separation of the interdependent variables into independent variables for what may be considered mathematical convenience. The concept of congestion factor is poorly explained and difficult to measure in any quantifiable or consistent manner. The concept of recognition being dependent on the number of resolvable cells across the smallest dimension of the object is clearly in conflict with other researchers, who claim that recognition is dependent on target area rather than a single dimension. The dependence on Johnson in relation to the same term also leaves some question of model validity. The model was never verified with field results. The strength of the model is that it recognizes the importance of search and mathematically describes the benefit of an *a priori* cue to the observer. Further, it recognizes the input of both clutter and noise as degradation factors on the detection process.

8.2.4   The GAVID Model

Originated by E. K. Seyb in the early 1970s, the GAVID (ground to air visual detection) model [3] is one of the most interesting of all visual detection models to incorporate search into the overall process. It not only incorporates generalized search but allows for a number of different types of search patterns. The effect of different forms of systematic search can be estimated as distinct from the usual assumption of random positions of the visual axis for a given fixation period. The model is further different from most models in that it is a Monte Carlo type model. The model uses a variation of the visual lobe detection concept.

Seyb's detection probability is based on the relationship of the received (reduced) contrast, C, due to the atmosphere to the contrast threshold, C_{FT}, of the eye. The latter is dependent upon the angular size of the target subtended at the eye, thus

$$C_{FT} = a + \frac{b}{\alpha - 0.6} \tag{8.9}$$

where

$a = 0.0055$
$b = 0.134$
$\alpha = $ the target subtense in minutes of arc.

The received target contrast, C, is given by

$$C = C_0 \left\{ 1 - SG \left[1 - \exp\left(3.91 \frac{R}{V_m} \right) \right] \right\}^{-1} \tag{8.10}$$

where

$C_0 = $ the intrinsic target contrast
$SG = B_s/B_0$ (the sky-ground ratio)
$B_s = $ the sky luminance
$B_0 = $ the background luminance
$R = $ the target range (km)
$V_m = $ the meteorological visibility (km).

Note: *Meteorological range* is defined here as the range at which the received contrast is reduced to 2% of its originating value. For further details concerning this algorithm see Section 5.2.1.1.

Seyb combines (8.9) and (8.10) to provide the probability of seeing in a glimpse (or fixation) as

$$P_s = 1 - 0.5^{(F_H CR)^3}$$ (8.11)

where

F_H = a human factor, from 0.5 to 1
CR = C/C_{FT}

Additionally Seyb allows for detection off the visual axis where C_{FT} is replaced by C_{PFT}, the contrast threshold for peripheral vision; thus,

$$C_{PFT} = C_{FT}\left(1 + \frac{\theta - 0.6}{\sqrt{\alpha}}\right)$$ (8.12)

where θ is the angle in degrees between the visual axis and the line from the eye to the center of the target.

GAVID starts out by finding the maximum detection range by equating the received contrast to the contrast threshold, and solving for the range, R_{max}, at which this occurs. The Monte Carlo simulation is then initiated at range R_m, where R_m is the minimum of the maximum range, R_{max} and the unmasked range, R_{unm}. A flight path of the target is assumed. The user can select any number from over a dozen search procedures from the familiar random through to systematic search both horizontal, vertical, boxcar, left to right, or right to left. Searches can start from the same initial position or from some random position. The model steps through at a single fixation interval and ascertains starting at R_m the received contrast, the range, and the offset from the visual axis in both horizontal and vertical axes at each fixation. It then calculates the probability of detection in each given fixation, and accumulates all single fixation probabilities from range R_m. The model makes a number of runs for a given search methodology with different initial conditions and averages the results.

The pioneering work of Seyb in addressing the complex area of search represents a milestone in visual modeling, and his work has been used as a cornerstone in the work of others (ourselves included) in the area of modeling the search process. His work set out to demonstrate the influence of having experienced personnel go through a systematic search rather than the assumed random search of an untrained observer. He not only demonstrated that there was a good theoretical basis for showing an improvement but he was able to quantify this and correlate the theory with field results. The model provides results that seem intuitively correct as regards optimal selections of fields of view of optical systems. In models that do not address the uncertainty associated with a search, the highest probability of detection is associated with maximum magnification; that is, the narrowest field of view. For any search sector there is obviously a compromise in terms of efficiency of search coverage (i.e., probability of looking in the correct direction) *versus* probability of detection given that one is looking in the appropriate direction. Seyb's model allows the system designer to quantify the value of cuing and to select an optimal field of view with respect to that cuing accuracy. Seyb's model also makes the vital link of including search time or elapsed time together with the associated probability of detection (and range). Again it seems an intuitively correct concept that the longer one searches for an object in a scene the more likely one is to observe it (given that the object is to some degree observable). Seyb's work is even more remarkable considering the year in which it was produced. Most of the basic concepts regarding visual lobe detection and search are very extendible to other models and would indeed bring new dimensions to some present static models.

8.3 NIGHT VISION LAB SUITE

The period 1975 to 1990 saw the introduction of a suite of electro-optical performance models from the U.S. Army laboratory known sequentially over the years as *Night Vision Lab* (NVL), *Night Vision and Electro-Optics Lab* (NVEOL), and CECOM *Center for Night Vision and Electro-Optics* (C2NVEOL). These have become standards within the U.S. defense industry, despite their shortcomings.

8.3.1 NVL Static Performance (Ratches) Model

The Night Vision Lab's static performance model for thermal viewing systems (FLIRs) is the earliest of the series and illustrates many of the features of the other models within the suite. It is also often called the *Ratches model*, after the primary author [4]. This model logically breaks down into two rather independent parts: a calculation of the system summary performance measure of MRTD (see Chapter 6), and a calculation of the acquisition probabilities for the particular situation input by the user. The former is considerably more detailed and sophisticated than the latter.

The FLIR system is characterized essentially by its MRTD curve (20 points). The user has the option of entering a measured curve or entering detailed system data and letting the program calculate the curve. Of course, if the first option is exercised, the program runs much faster. In this case, the user is still required to enter some detailed system data, but none of it makes any difference in the output except the value entered for horizontal instantaneous field of view (DELTAX) in milliradians: this value determines the spatial frequency increment (XL) for the MRTD points by

$$XL = (20 \text{ DELTAX})^{-1} \qquad\qquad (8.13)$$

In the more usual case of detailed system entry, system descriptors required can include wavelength band, optics F-number, optics focal length, optics transmission, optics MTF data, instantaneous fields of view, number of detectors in parallel and series, detector size, peak D^* and the temporal frequency at which it was measured, cold shield angle, type of limiting noise, 3 dB cutoff of detector temporal frequency response, frame rate, scan efficiency, overscan ratio, frequency of preamp 3 dB cuton, frequency of amplifier 3 dB cutoff, electronic boost amplitude and frequency, display type, average display brightness, display MTF data, horizontal and vertical fields of view, system magnification, ratio of wide to narrow field of view, stabilization MTF data, various MTF curves in temporal or spatial frequencies, noise power spectrum curve, or D_λ^* curve *versus* wavelength. Although the entry of some of these values may obviate the necessity of entering others, it is still easy to see why the user might prefer to find a measured MRTD curve for the system of interest.

Once the program has a system MRTD curve at hand, the rest of the model is exceedingly simple. The background and target are characterized only by a background temperature, target temperature difference, and target length and height. Therefore only blackbodies are modeled or at least only blackbody equivalent temperatures.

The atmospherics incorporate LOWTRAN 2 and thus represent an advance over pre-1970 models. Inputs required are air temperature, relative humidity, and visibility range. Four discrete rain scenarios may be used as well.

The human observer is characterized by default values of a threshold SNR and eye integration time, which may be changed by the user. These are used in the MRTD calculation. In addition the program contains default acquisition probability *versus* resolved cycles across the target curves, incorporating Johnson's criteria at the 50% points. These may also be altered by the user.

In the model algorithms, the target temperature difference is simply multiplied by an atmospheric transmittance to obtain what is in effect a "received" temperature difference, ΔT_c. Then the MRTD curve is really used as a maximum resolvable cycle curve, because the received ΔT_c is entered into the curve to arrive at a spatial frequency: the maximum spatial frequency resolvable at that temperature difference. That maximum spatial frequency in cycles per milliradian is multiplied by the angular size in milliradians of the target at the range in question to obtain resolvable cycles across the target. Finally the internal probability curves are accessed to get acquisition probabilities. This algorithm is so simple, that if we started with the MRTD curve and a separate LOWTRAN run, we would hardly need a computer to do the rest of the calculations.

The model is rather badly mismatched in its parts, being fairly rigorous in its system modeling and very much oversimplified in almost all the rest of its modeling (except perhaps for using LOWTRAN to find atmospheric transmission). The user may choose a long form output, which produces a second detection probability based on signal-to-noise ratio and Rosell and Willson data. This second detection probability invariably decreases with range much more slowly than the first based on Johnson's criterion. The documentation suggests that the discrepancy is due to the first probability being applicable to cluttered backgrounds whereas the second is applicable to uniform backgrounds. Of course, the original model assumption of an observer looking directly at the target position (no search) belies this explanation: clutter can make little difference if all the observer has to do is decide if there is an object at some given position. The real reason for the discrepancy is clearly the different experimental bases for Johnson's criteria and Rosell and Willson's data. As noted in Section 7.2.2, Rosell and Willson themselves asserted that predictions based on Johnson's criteria would be more pessimistic than field experiments.

The documentation of the model does include a validation section, describing the results of four field tests done in 1971 and 1973, as well as laboratory measurements of MRTD. Four of the model curves shown (recognition probability *versus* range) show good fits to the experimental data, one shows a fair fit, and six show poor fits, with most of the latter having significant underestimates of performance by the model. On the other hand, the curves presented that show model predictions of MRTD and experimental measurements of the same generally show good results. No statistical analysis of the results was attempted.

8.3.2 Image Intensifier Performance Model

This model has origins dating back to 1969, but we are specifically discussing the 1985 version [5]. It will model the performance of an observer using an image intensifier, the unaided eye, or the eye aided by direct-view optics, making it more versatile than the FLIR models. Like the Ratches model, it is a static model: the target and sensor are stationary and the observer is already looking directly at the target. It is also very similar to the previous model in its overall approach to the acqusition problem, only with a quantity called *minimum resolvable contrast* playing the role of MRTD. An inherent contrast is propagated through the atmosphere to provide a received contrast at the sensor, which itself is characterized by its MRC curve. The received contrast and MRC relationship together allow the calculation of maximum resolvable frequency, which in turn leads to acquisition probabilities through the TTPF (see Table 7.3). As before, much of the calculation is devoted to the MRC calculation to characterize the system; however, the other submodels here are closer in sophistication to the system submodel.

In this model target and background menus are provided from which the user may choose 1 of 7 backgrounds and 1 of 11 target types. Internally stored tables of spectral reflectance can then be accessed by the program. This input option is a very useful device to make the program user friendly, and the stored tables mean that the target and background submodel is a step up in sophistication from the Ratches model. The only other required target input is a critical dimension. Because we work with reflected radiation in the visible part of the spectrum, scene illuminance must also be an input.

As in the Ratches model, atmospherics are based on LOWTRAN 2, and required input consists of air temperature, relative humidity, and visibility. In this case, because of the shorter wavelengths involved, an attempt is made to specifically take in-scattering into account in calculating the transmitted contrast. The total atmospheric transmittance, τ, and the scattering transmittance, τ_s, are called out separately from LOWTRAN. The received radiance (from target or background) is taken essentially as

$$L_R = L_{sky}[\rho\tau + (1 - \tau_s)] \tag{8.14}$$

where

L_{sky} = sky radiance
ρ = reflectance (target or background).

The term $1 - \tau_s$ in (8.14) adds to both target and background and, therefore, decreases contrast monotonically as scattering increases. However, no justification is given in the documentation for the specific form of (8.14), and we must examine the actual code to even find this algorithm.

If the sensor modeled is just the unaided eye, then no system input is required. In direct view optics, only the optical system magnification and transmittance are called for (no MTF input). Of course, to model an image intensifier a great deal more input data is required. This data includes objective focal length, objective T-number, transmittance of eyepiece, system magnification, luminous gain, tube noise figure, maximum brightness of output phosphor, transfer factor, equivalent brightness input, system MTF data, photocathode spectral responsivity curve, and any filter transmittance curves.

For any one of the three cases modeled, the crux of the model calculations is in the algorithm for maximum resolvable frequency (called *subjective resolution*) from the MRC. Unfortunately it is precisely this algorithm that is referenced to undated, unpublished, internal NVL reports. Even the expression relating subjective resolution to MRC for the unaided eye is so complicated that it must be solved iteratively within the program, and it contains some fixed, assumed values for quantities like eye integration time and threshold SNR. For the eye aided by *direct view optics* (DVO), the only change is in scaling the spatial frequency by the magnification and reducing the luminance by the transmittance. A similar relation between subjective resolution and MRC is used in the case of viewing through an image intensifier, only here the system MTF and noise characteristics must be taken into account. The weakness of going right from resolvable cycles across the target to acquisition probability has already been commented upon in Chapter 7.

The documentation does contain a small validation section, with six calculated curves and corresponding experimental points for MRC as a function of frequency: three each for the unaided eye and an image intensifier system. The agreement between theory and experiment looks fairly good. Also, calculations were done for two target sizes of Blackwell's data over a restricted luminance range, and the calculated contrast threshold plotted superimposed on Blackwell's data. Presumably calculated MRC was assumed identical with threshold contrast, but it is left unclear how spatial frequencies of periodic targets in the model convert to Blackwell's target sizes. One of these curves shows good agreement, whereas the other could be characterized only as fair. One suspects that in the curves shown, the best data was selected, as the text frankly admits that comprehensive validation is lacking and even that some data is contradictory.

8.3.3 FLIR90

In June 1990, C2NVEO introduced their long-awaited replacement of the 1975 Ratches model for simulating the performance of thermal imaging systems. This model, FLIR90, has many similarities to the earlier one, but it makes explicit the dichotomy that was only implicit in Ratches: one series of calculations results in an MRTD curve for the system specified, whereas a second independent series models everything else about the acquisition problem, characterizing the system completely by the MRTD curve. FLIR90 is actually divided into two independent parts requiring separate computer runs. The first part is called FLIR90 (lending its name to the whole model), and the second accepts MRTD output from this first and is named *ACQUIRE*. If the system MRTD is already known, then ACQUIRE may be run alone to arrive at acquisition probabilities. FLIR90, the system model, is several steps above the Ratches model in sophistication; whereas ACQUIRE, if anything, represents a regression from Ratches.

The FLIR90 part of the new model provides an input data file template that can be customized to the user's specific system with any screen editor. This new feature is flexible and convenient. The system is described by input variables like those of the Ratches model, with the addition of several new options. Both a prefilter and postfilter MTF curve can now be added to the system description, as well as an extra Gaussian MTF curve and an extra sinc MTF curve (primarily to simulate a CCD readout). A run of the system FLIR90 produces two output files, one with extension .OUT, which shows the input and the system measures calculated, and another with extension .ACQ, which is a template input file for

ACQUIRE with the MRTD values filled in. FLIR90 now makes a nod to the idea of target *area* as a critical factor, by calculating both x and y MRTD curves and a 2-D MRTD curve from them; all three are sent to both the .OUT and .ACQ files. The 2-D MRTD is calculated by taking the x and y spatial frequencies at a given value of MRTD and finding the geometric mean of those frequencies. The MRTD value in question is then plotted against this geometric mean frequency to obtain the 2-D MRTD curve, which will lie between the two 1-D curves. Although not unreasonable, this procedure receives no justification in the documentation.

To model the actual acquisition problem scenario, ACQUIRE has the inputs of only target height and length, target ΔT, atmospheric transmittance, and any smoke effects. Except for the ability to consider smoke, this description of the scene represents a step backward from the Ratches model, which itself was not known for sophistication in this portion of its modeling. For example, a LOWTRAN version is no longer contained within the model, but instead the atmospheric transmittance in km^{-1} must be entered by the user, who is left to his or her own devices to ascertain this value. If we have access to LOWTRAN, a separate run for the conditions of interest may be made, but the transmittance values returned by LOWTRAN do not always conform to the exponential law implied by the ACQUIRE assumption that one value of transmittance per km suffices. Guided by Johnson's criteria, resolvable cycles across the target critical dimension still solely determine acquisition probability. However, now with a two-dimensional MRTD curve, fewer cycles are deemed to be necessary for a given level of acquisition (see Table 8.3) and the square root of target area is taken as the critical dimension.

Considered overall, FLIR90 probably represents a considerable advance in thermal imaging system performance *measure* modeling, but little improvement in field performance modeling over the earlier Ratches model.

8.4 OTHER CONTEMPORARY MODELS

8.4.1 VOM

At I-MATH Associates, under the leadership of A. Akerman, a number of individual models have been combined to form their *visual observer model* (VOM). The individual models for scene, sensor, and human observer date back to the latter half of the 1970s.

The scene model, called *LASER +*, was originally designed to simulate aircraft targets against the sky. In addition to target size and average contrast, LASER + is designed to take into account such factors as glint from the aircraft canopy and pattern within the target. Akerman and associates have been adapting the model to ground targets by considering such items as background texture and

Table 8.3
2-D Cycle Criteria for
Recognition

Probability	# Cycles
.90	5.5
.70	4
.50	3
.30	2.3
.10	1.5

ground shadows. The most striking aspect of this work is the great care taken to consider all aspects of the problem and avoid unjustified generalizations, an attitude often lacking in model builders.

If an EO sensor is used, then the submodel GEOSS (generic EO sensor simulator) is called. This module takes into account optics, detector, and electronic MTFs, and electronic noise to simulate the displayed image. In the case of the unaided eye, this module is skipped.

The human observer submodel is called VIDEM [6] for visual detection model. It is basically a modification of the MARSAM model. Referring back to Section 7.3.2, the reader may remember that detection probability in MARSAM was formed from four component probabilities (leaving out line-of-sight probability). P_2, the probability that the observer makes a fixation on the target in the specified time, was considered to be a function of P_3, the probability that the target will be correctly discriminated from confusing objects. Then the detection probability in MARSAM was the product of P_1, the probability of sufficient target size and contrast for detection, P_2, and P_4, the probability of sufficient signal-to-noise for detection. VIDEM makes an important alteration in this algorithm: P_1 and P_2 are replaced by a cumulative detection probability, P_{cum}, which is calculated from target size and contrast and the nature of the visual search, taking into account search time and off-axis detection. Then detection probability is calculated by

$$P_D = P_{cum} P_3 P_4 \tag{8.15}$$

To calculate P_{cum}, a parafoveal contrast threshold is modeled by

$$C_T = 0.0352 \, \theta^{0.24} + 0.584 \, \theta^{1.6}/\alpha^2 \tag{8.16}$$

where

θ = angle off foveal axis in degrees ($\geq 0.8°$)
α = displayed target angular size in minutes.

Now, using (8.16), a single-glimpse probability is calculated as in (7.9). An average detection probability, g, is then calculated from the weighted average of the single-glimpse probabilities, each weight being the probability of occurrence of that particular value of θ and going to 0 for angles outside the search sector. Finally, the detection probability is accumulated over time in the usual manner, assuming random search:

$$P_{cum}(n) = P_{cum}(n - 1) + [1 - P_{cum}(n - 1)]g_n \tag{8.17}$$

where n is the number of fixations in the search time.

Thus VIDEM attempts to account for contrast, size, and search within the P_{cum} term, clutter within the P_g term, and SNR within the P_4 term. This approach is considerably advanced compared to most of the human models we have previously described; although, as we noted in Section 7.3.2, there is room for doubt concerning the separability of these influences. The recognition algorithm follows MARSAM closely. VOM even contains a color contrast submodel called *COCO*, which may be called if the user wants to play that variable. COCO contains an algorithm to calculate effective contrast from luminance and chromatic contrasts, based on a limited set of empirical data for sky and aircraft paint colors. Overall, VOM is characterized by great care in its construction, imaginative and advanced concepts, and a firm basis in experimental data.

8.4.2 TTIM

The *TACOM thermal image model* (TTIM) [7], developed during the late 1980s, is a model that generates synthetic images to estimate overall probabilities of detection and recognition. Although attributed to the efforts of many, G. Gerhart is the driving force behind the model. Again one looks to the origins and issues that faced the originators to establish the nature of the model. This model reflects the strong image processing capability of Gerhart's group at TACOM, and their resolve to discover more about the impact of target signature on acquisition performance. Most acquisition models treat the target and background as homogeneous entities, the former being nominally a uniform rectangle superimposed on the latter. TACOM was interested in developing a model that could predict a tank's signature and embed that signature in a scene. The strength of TTIM is that it builds on, and is a collection of, a series of first principles models. A reduced block diagram of TTIM is shown as Figure 8.2 [8]. The model starts with the design layout of a military vehicle. A CAD/CAM file is produced that is passed to PRISM, which calculates the surface temperatures of isothermal facets on the vehicle. PRISM [9] incorporates sky, terrain, and atmospheric calculations. The output of PRISM is a faceted, IR-signature model of the vehicle.

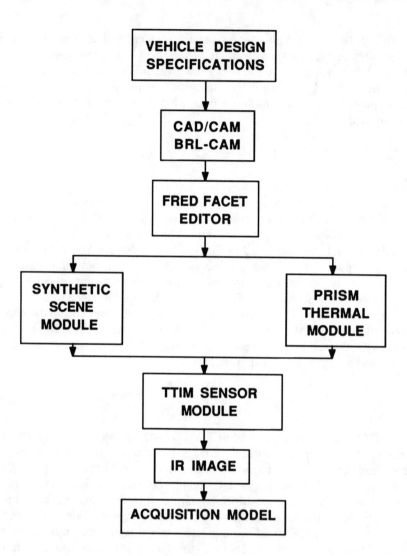

Figure 8.2 Block diagram of TTIM.

This target model is embedded in a natural or synthetically generated scene. The result is a target and background radiance map. The output of this is in turn passed to the sensor module from the C2NVEO static performance model. The output of this module is a pixel-by-pixel map of the input radiance as would be seen by a thermal imaging sensor. This output is either displayed or passed to an acquisition module based on Johnson's criteria.

This model is considerably different from the other models discussed. It deals with the particular case rather than the generalized case. Nevertheless it is an end-to-end model. Its strength lies in the ability to model and produce radiant maps of future (projected) vehicles before they are built. In this manner the designer can iterate new designs to reduce the signature of vehicles. PRISM allows us to view the vehicle signature at any time of the day under a number of conditions. Its strength from the perspective of a detailed design tool for evaluating signature reduction effects may also be considered a weakness in terms of a tool for use as a target acquisition sensor design tool.

8.4.3 The PHIND Model

PHIND (photons in noise detectability) is intended to be not one but a series of target acquisition models developed at TNO Institute for Perception in the Netherlands. The original PHIND was developed in 1987 principally by J. J. Vos and A. van Meeteren [10, 11]. It produced target acquisition range as a function of light level, using physical instrument data and meteorological range as parameters. Its more recent form is PHIND89 [12] which generates target acquisition range as function of distance.

PHIND attempts to understand the driving factors that influence detection. Those factors were originally addressed by van Meeteren in his doctoral dissertation. He returns to the spatial domain and shows that recognition is essentially detection of a characteristic part of the object under consideration. This characteristic length is different for *each* object class, but the concept aligns with the work of others in the field and compares favorably with the Air Force Standardization Agreement [13] for characteristic lengths of vehicles. Vos and van Meeteren's scathing comments, regarding most of the target acquisition models as pragmatic interpolation programs "requiring prototype testing rather than predictive models based on theoretical concepts," appear well founded. Their work clearly lays out the theoretical basis and supports the analysis with considerable experimental data.

The model is developed principally for image intensifier systems, although its authors claim it can be extended to the unaided eye and optical and electro-optical aids. Time to detect is not explicitly expressed in any equation within the model. Time is implicit in the theoretical basis and represents an effective perception time of 0.1 second. Search is not a variable within the model. All calculations are related to foveal vision and do not involve search.

The model starts in a logical fashion with the target observed against its background. However, as distinct from the majority of target models, van Meeteren has defined a number of target-background descriptions in terms of their characteristic dimensions (or detail), α_{CH}, and the contrast of the characteristic detail, C_{CH}, to be used for recognition. Table 8.4 gives typical values. Note that contrast

Table 8.4
PHIND Characteristic Detail and Contrast

Target	$d_{ch}(m)$	C_{ch}
Board-Tent	0.7	10
Vehicles	0.7	2
Human-Shrub	0.7	0.5

is defined in the usual terms of background luminance less target luminance divided by background luminance. Using the intrinsic contrast of the characteristic detail as the starting point, PHIND estimates at what range observers will be expected to see these characteristic details by their contrast sensitivity. PHIND assumes this range is "determined by the noise in the effective photon catch from the visible scene."

Reemphasizing that PHIND was developed for prediction of target acquisition distance with image intensifiers, the model assumes the system to have an objective lens of diameter D_1, absorption of the optics, τ_{op}, and a cathode sensitivity of S_{ka} in amps/lumen. Then from a scene of average luminance the model calculates the retinal excitation due to the effective number of photons received at the cathode of the intensifier. This calculation includes a loss factor, f, which accommodates the case of insufficient amplification to yield a retinal excitation for every received photon. Empirical relationships for f are derived for both foveal vision and, at lower light levels, for parafoveal, scotopic vision. PHIND then calculates the total photon count integrated for 100 ms from the characteristic detail, d_{ch}, at a distance r.

From here there are two considerations. The first case deals with the situation where the target is not at a range, r_{cr}, at which the target detail would exceed the resolution limit of the system; and the second case is when it is beyond this range. Dealing with the first case, the contrast sensitivity is governed by the square root of the photon noise limitation (Piper's law):

$$S_r \leq r_{cr} = 3.5 \times 10^8 \frac{d_{ch}}{r} D_1 \sqrt{\rho_{sc} \tau_{op} S_{ka} f(E_v - E_{thr})} \tag{8.18}$$

where

E_{thr} = threshold illuminance
ρ_{sc} = scene reflectance
E_v = scene illuminance.

Beyond r_{cr} the target is a point source, and for it to be detectable, the number of photons reaching the eye has to be constant (Ricco's law); therefore,

$$S_r > r_{cr} = 3.5 \times 10^8 \, d_{ch} \, \frac{r_{cr}}{r^2} \, D_1 \, \sqrt{\rho_{sc} \, T_{op} \, S_{ka} \, f(E_v - E_{thr})} \qquad (8.19)$$

Equations (8.18) and (8.19) determine the contrast sensitivity at a given range and light level. The sensitivity, S_{re}, required to see the characteristic detail is

$$S_{re} = 1/C_{ch}$$

This equation assumes a signal-to-noise ratio of 1:1 and that the intrinsic contrast has not been reduced by meteorological conditions. To accommodate other signal-to-noise ratios, PHIND introduces a variable d', which can be chosen by the system evaluator. A typical value for d' appears to be 4. To accommodate contrast reduction due to atmospheric effects, the characteristic contrast is reduced thus

$$C' = \frac{C_{ch}}{1 + (2/\rho_{sc}) \, [\exp(3r/V) - 1]} \qquad (8.20)$$

Therefore the required sensitivity to yield acquisition is

$$S_{re} = \frac{d'}{C_{ch}} \left\{ 1 + \frac{2}{\rho_{sc}} \, [\exp(3r/V) - 1] \right\} \qquad (8.21)$$

To calculate acquisition distances, it becomes necessary to match contrast sensitivity of the system to the received contrast from the characteristic detail contrast (multiplied by d'):

$$r_{ac} = r_{cr} \left\{ \frac{S_{cr} C_{ch}}{d' \, [20 \, \exp(3r_{ac}/V) - 19]} \right\}^{\beta} \qquad (8.22)$$

where

$$\beta = \begin{cases} 0.5 & r_{ac} < r_{cr} \\ 1 & r_{ac} \geq r_{cr} \end{cases}$$

Equations (8.18) and (8.19) reflect the strength of PHIND as a model.

Together they provide the contrast threshold-sensitivity of the system as a function of light level, object size, and measurable system parameters. The work on describing targets and backgrounds as a characteristic detail of size and contrast is unique, and the basis is the result of considerable experimental data. What seems to be a particular result is that d_{ch} appears to be approximately constant for vehicles at around 0.7 m. In their earlier work, van Meeteren and Vos left the variable d' as 2, 4, or 6 for detection, recognition, and identification, respectively.

The PHIND model is a thorough theoretical analysis backed up by considerable experimentation. Where van Meeteren and Vos have resorted to empirical fits to experimental data, they have clearly indicated so. The resulting overall formulation has been experimentally tested and the results shown indicate good comparison between the PHIND model and experimental data. The model should be commended also for the remarkable simplicity of the final results. The preceding equations require a very modest computer to automate system calculations. The model is not applicable to the infrared band, nor does it provide for search, nevertheless it is a remarkable model.

8.4.4 VISDET and IRDET

This book would not be complete without the inclusion of two models developed by us, one covering the visual band and one covering the infrared band. VISDET [14] was initially developed in 1979 in conjunction with H. D. Nelgner. The same three researchers initiated development of infrared models in 1980, which led to the first IRDET around 1981. IRDET [15] evolved from two earlier models developed by us: KRUDET, based on the Kruse atmospheric model (see Section 5.2.3), and LOWDET, based on LOWTRAN. IRDET uses EOSAEL for its atmospherics and a good deal of its radiometrics. VISDET, covering visible wavelengths, and IRDET, covering infrared wavelengths, are described here.

VISDET models the detection or recognition performance of a human observer using the unaided eye, a telescopic sight, or a TV system against a stationary or horizontally moving target, whereas IRDET does the same for an observer using a thermal imaging system (FLIR). Both models incorporate search and motion-enhanced contrast (see Section 7.2.4) for detection (not for recognition). Either program may be fed values from a previously built and edited input file or by an interactive screen input file builder. In either case the output for a stationary target is in the form of detection or recognition probability *versus* range for a given search time, or the user may select a matrix output form that shows acquisition probability as a function of both range (columns) and time (rows). For a rapidly moving target (e.g., high-speed aircraft), range and time become interdependent variables so the models deliver acquisition probability *versus* time and the corresponding range, shown in two adjacent columns.

8.4.4.1 VISDET

The scene submodel of VISDET requires the input of the ambient illumination condition, a choice of sky or terrain background, target and background (in the case of terrain) reflectances, target size, and target motion. The ambient illumination is entered by user choice from a menu of 10 descriptive conditions; illuminance values for each condition are stored internally. In the case of sky background, the program accesses an internally stored table of sky radiances, one for each of the descriptive conditions in the ambient illumination menu, so no background reflectance is requested by the submodel.

The target and terrain background are treated very simply as Lambertian reflectors, and a single value of reflectance is assumed to be sufficient for the whole visible band. The submodel calculates target and background luminances at zero range by the photometric analog of (4.3):

$$L_r = \rho E_s / \pi \tag{8.23}$$

where

L_r = reflected luminance
ρ = average reflectance across visible band
E_s = scene illuminance.

The output from the submodel consists of target and background luminances at zero range and inherent contrast.

The atmospheric submodel is just the simple visible algorithm of Section 5.2.1. It requires the additional user inputs of range, visibility (meteorological range), precipitation rate and type, and transmittance through battlefield-induced contaminants. Because range is considered an independent variable, it is entered as a minimum, maximum, and range step for a stationary or slow-moving target: the program cycles from minimum to maximum in increments equal to the range step. In the case of a fast-moving target, range is tied to time, which is stepped in 1 second increments. If the target is of this type, the program requests only an initial range to start the calculations and a minimum ground range. The visibility entry is meant to be the value applicable if precipitation and BIC are absent, because these effects are calculated separately. The precipitation algorithm follows (5.42), (5.46), and (5.47) of Section 5.2.6. The BIC transmittance entry must be calculated off-line by the user, for example, by a separate run of the appropriate EOSAEL module. The atmospheric submodel delivers received (at the specified range) target and background luminances and received contrast. Target angular size at the specified range is also calculated.

The VISDET user has three possible system choices from a menu: the unaided eye, a telescopic sight (direct-view optics), or a TV system. If the first option is chosen, no other system input is requested, because all the eye's characteristics are contained internal to the program.

For direct view optics (DVO) the user must enter objective aperture and F-number, optical MTF data, field of view, magnification, optics transmittance, and rms amplitude of line-of-sight vibration. The optical MTF entry itself offers the user a menu that includes diffraction-limited optics, input of the single-value figure of merit of the Strehl ratio (see Section 6.2.4), or just the MTF value at some specified spatial frequency. In the latter two cases, a polynomial or Gaussian approximation is used for the MTF. The received luminances are reduced by the optics transmittance, and the received contrast is reduced by the MTF value corresponding to target size (including vibration MTF), thus producing displayed luminance and contrast. Displayed target angular size follows from magnification.

A TV system requires the following inputs: optics aperture, F-number, and transmittance, optics MTF data, field of view, data on limiting resolution *versus* faceplate illumination, display luminance, size and MTF data, viewer distance, and rms amplitude of line-of-sight vibration. The optics data is used to calculate the target contrast and illuminance in the image on the tube faceplate. The latter value allows the program to enter the system resolution curve to find the limiting resolution. The limiting resolution is used as a 3% MTF point to establish a Gaussian system MTF curve. This curve could be used to characterize the whole system, camera to monitor, as limiting resolution curves can be measured only by an observer looking at some display. However, a separate MTF entry is available for the display, so that the effects of changing just the display can be investigated; a user who wants the limiting resolution *versus* faceplate illumination curve to represent the whole system including display should enter a very high resolution for the monitor. A middle gray shade is assumed for the displayed background luminance (see Section 6.4.2), and the system MTF value for the target size reduces the received contrast to produce the displayed contrast. Field of view, display size, target size, and the viewer distance from the display allows a simple geometric calculation of the target displayed angular size.

These results of displayed target contrast, size, and luminance are fed to the human observer submodel, which is just the spatial domain empirical model of Section 7.3.4. A perusal of that section should convince the reader that it shares many affinities with the GAVID and VIDEM models described earlier in this chapter. The former similarity is not surprising because GAVID was one of the influences in the development of our models; but the latter is an example of independent lines of reasoning arriving at similar results. One difference is that the effects of clutter do not enter as a separate factor as in VIDEM, but are included within the cumulative probability calculation in the human factor value. This human factor value is one of the inputs required by this submodel, along with search time for a stationary target, and search sector. Acquisition probability is accumulated for the whole search time at each range for a stationary (or slow-moving) target, but for a fast-moving target the range changes with each time step of the accumulation. Recognition is treated as detection of a smaller detail (a la van Meeteren) in a search narrowed down to just the target itself (no input of search sector is required for recognition), and so this recognition is conditional on prior detection and may well have a higher probability than detection, depending on the search problem.

8.4.4.2   IRDET

As noted earlier, IRDET makes generous use of EOSAEL modules (see Section 5.25). These modules allow IRDET to model the battlefield environment, including smoke and dust, more realistically. The germinal equation for IRDET (and LOW-DET) was taken from a 1980 paper by Kahle, Madura, and Soha [16]:

$$LR_\lambda = [\epsilon_\lambda L_{BB\lambda} + (1 - \epsilon_\lambda) L_{s\lambda}] \tau_\lambda + L_{p\lambda} \tag{8.24}$$

where

LR_λ = received spectral radiance at range R
ϵ_λ = spectral emissivity (target or background)
$L_{BB\lambda}$ = blackbody spectral radiance at temperature T
$L_{s\lambda}$ = spectral radiance from sky
τ_λ = spectral transmittance of atmosphere
$L_{p\lambda}$ = path spectral radiance.

Equation (8.24) is an elaboration of (5.9), in that it includes reflected sky radiance in the second term inside the brackets, and the additive radiance term at the end (path radiance) may include emitted as well as in-scattered radiance.

   We found that the SPOT and COMBIC modules of EOSAEL 82 would automatically calculate many of the terms of (8.24) if the input to them is correctly ordered. The scene input required of the user includes latitude and longitude, season and time of day, spectral emissivities and temperatures of target and background, size of target, and position and motion of target relative to the sensor. The latitude, longitude, season, and time of day inputs allow IRDET to choose the atmospheric option and compute the sun position for input to EOSAEL. The geometry of the situation is explained on the screen to the user, who then has the option of proceeding or changing the scenario. The use of spectral emissivities allows for more general sources than just blackbodies. To facilitate input, menus of common targets and backgrounds are provided so that the user can call upon internally stored spectral curves. IRDET carries 10–20 spectral points in its calculations.

The use of EOSAEL modules combines the scene and atmospheric submodels. To describe the atmosphere the user must enter visibility, aerosol choice (from a menu), precipitation input, and choices for BIC. The precipitation input and algorithms are the same as for VISDET. The user who chooses to exercise the BIC option must enter quite a bit more data to describe the situation to be modeled, including wind and cloud conditions. The BIC option can simulate the effects of various types of screening smokes, dust from high explosives, or vehicular dust. The temporal nature of smoke and dust is simulated by switching to the dynamic mode of probability accumulation used for rapidly moving targets: the average one-glimpse probability is updated every time step of 1 second. The final results sent to the system submodel are the received spectral radiances from target and background.

The system includes the sensor, electronics, and display. The sensor portion of the model follows radiance through the optics to the detectors, and there it does a spectral integration to calculate signal output (actually signal-to-noise ratio). Input required of the user includes optics aperture, optics F-number, optics transmittance, FOV, optics MTF options, frame rate, scanning choice from a menu, scan efficiency, spectral detectivity, detector size and number, and rms amplitude of LOS vibration. The input of a spectral detectivity curve is aided by a menu of HgCdTe choices at different temperatures. Equation (6.93) is essentially the one used to find SNR, except that with ac-coupled systems, the signal radiance is the difference between target and background radiances.

From the display submodel, we are trying to find displayed target size and contrast, and background luminance, to use the same human observer submodel to calculate acquisition probability. The user must enter MTF data, maximum and average display luminances, display size, and dynamic range in gray shades (see (6.112)). We assume the detector noise is the limiting noise for the system and that the SNR value calculated at the detector output is essentially that available in the signal to the display. This would be nearly true for a well-designed electronic system. Because rms noise appears on top of both the target and background, the SNR value limits the effective contrast that can be presented by the display. The display settings are assumed to be such that the maximum effective contrast consistent with the SNR and display MTF is what is actually displayed. Then the human submodel of Section 7.3.4 can be used to find acquisition probabilities.

IRDET is not as strong as the NVL models in characterizing the FLIR system and could certainly benefit from the use of a summary performance measure like MRTD or MDTD to simplify system input. On the other hand, IRDET is considerably more balanced in its overall treatment, allowing more sophisticated target and background characterization and the simulation of search. It has been compared to the Ratches model by limiting its scene to blackbodies (one menu choice) and its search sector to one fixation position on the target. In this case, it generally gives much more optimistic detection results than the MRTD-based detection results from Ratches, but its 10 s results are very similar to the latter's Rosell and Willson based results. In fact, IRDET detection results and Ratches's Rosell and Willson detection results are always much closer together than the latter's own two detection results. Another feature of IRDET is that detection and particularly the recognition probabilities fall off much more rapidly with range than those of the Ratches model.

8.5 CONCLUSION

Throughout this book we have stressed that models should be constructed and used with emphasis on the appropriate application. In this chapter we have given examples of a dozen or so models that were developed for various applications, each unique in its own way. Modelers sometimes look for the panacea of one model flexible and complete enough to undertake any acquisition simulation, but we feel that this is unrealistic. It is better to be armed with a number of models that, together with an understanding of the underlying assumptions, will allow the selection of the right model for the application. We hope this book has provided the reader with sufficient knowledge that, when faced with a modeling requirement, he or she can either select the most appropriate model or be capable of developing his or her own from the fundamentals described. If such is the case, then our labors have been worthwhile.

REFERENCES

1. "Target Acquisition Sensor Technology in the 1975–1985 Time Period," Naval Warfare Research Center Research Memo. NWRC RM-41, SRI Project 2167-320, November 1967.
2. H.H. Bailey, "Target Detection Through Visual Recognition," Rand Corp. Memo. RM6158/1-PR, February 1970.
3. E.K. Seyb, "Influence of Search Mode on Visual Detection of Airborne Targets," SHAPE Tech. Memo STC TM-458, 1975.
4. J.A. Ratches et al., "Night Vision Laboratory Static Performance Model for Thermal Viewing Systems," U.S. Army Electronics Command Tech. Rep. ECOM-7043, April 1975.
5. J.A. Leslie et al., "Reference and User's Manual for NV&EOL Visionics Division Image Intensifier Performance Model," U.S. Army Electronics R&D Command, April 1985.
6. A. Akerman and R. Kinzly, "Predicting Aircraft Detectability," *Human Factors*, Vol. 21, 1979, pp. 277–291.
7. T.J. Rogne, C.S. Hall, R. Freeling, and G.R. Gerhart, "U.S. Tank Automotive Command (TACOM) Thermal Image Model (TTIM)," *SPIE*, Vol. 1110, 1989.
8. G.R. Gerhart, "Low Observable Technology Development and Integration Through Signature Simulation and Modeling," *Combat Vehicle Survivability Symp. Proc.*, Vol. 2, March 1990.
9. W.R. Reynolds, "PRISM User's Manual, Version 2.0," Keewenaw Research Center, 1989.

10.   J.J. Vos and A. van Meeteren, "PHIND: An Analytical Model to Predict Target Acquisition Distance with Image Intensifiers," *Appl. Opt.*, Vol. 30, March 10, 1991, pp. 958–966.

11.   J.J. Vos and A. van Meeteren, TNO Report IZF 1989-45, TNO Defense Research, the Netherlands, 1989.

12.   J.J. Vos, TNO Report IZF 1989-46, TNO Defense Research, the Netherlands, 1989.

13.   "Minimum Ground Object Sizes for Imagery Interpretation," Air Force Standardization Agreement, Air Standardization Coordinating Committee, ASCC Air Std 101/8, December 31, 1976.

14.   G. Waldman, J. Wootton, and G. Hobson, "Visual Detection with Search: An Empirical Model," *IEEE Trans. on Systems, Man, and Cyber.*, Vol. 21, 1991, pp. 596–606.

15.   J. Wootton, G. Waldman, and K. Lauberg, "An IR Detection Program Incorporating EOSAEL," Fourth Annual EOSAEL Workshop, U.S. Army Electronics R&D Command, Atmospheric Sciences Laboratory, November 30, 1983.

16.   A. Kahle, D. Madura, and J. Soha, "Middle Infrared Multispectral Aircraft Scanner Data: Analysis for Geological Applications," *Appl. Opt.*, Vol. 19, July 15, 1980, pp. 2279–2290.

Index